F. A. Ficken

New York University, University Heights

The Simplex Method
of Linear Programming

HOLT, RINEHART AND WINSTON

New York

Preface

A few years ago the author, then at the University of Tennessee, was invited by specialists in engineering and business to prepare an account of the simplex method of linear programming. While a practically useful statement was not too difficult, there were many mathematical uncertainties. Though more recent literature has brought some clarification, there may still be a place for an exposition directed primarily to the mathematical theory of the method.

The course of the argument is indicated by the table of contents. An essential feature is the replacement (in Section 5) of the original problem by a closely related more tractable problem, called the "prepared problem," so chosen that a single discussion can dispose in a circumspect manner of all essential details. The solution of the dual problem, moreover, can always be found at a definite spot in the final tableau.

The prerequisite ideas are listed formally in Appendix I with an occasional word of explanation. Enough material has been supplied, it is hoped, to enable a moderately mature student without previous training in linear algebra to understand most of the text.

The bibliography is intended to provide an introduction to the literature. Some of the items—such as [7] and [15]—have comprehensive references.

No new results are claimed. Many features of our presentation now appear somewhere in the literature (especially in [7]), but there are certain details that we have not seen elsewhere. No attention has been given here to computational efficiency, and several of our steps have merely the aim of simplifying the notation or argument.

Our quite limited purpose has forced many regrettable omissions. We give in Section 7 an application to a problem in fuel-oil blending taken from [18]; that reference includes several other problems in linear programming arising from refinery operations. We also state a general allocation (maximum output) problem in Section 1. These allusions give only the merest hint of the scope and variety of problems involving linear programming. One of the earliest problems was the transportation or shipping problem: A manufacturer has a number of warehouses and factories and he knows the cost of shipping a unit of the product from each factory to each warehouse; he wishes to arrange shipments so that (1) the output of each factory will go to some warehouse, (2) the capacity of no warehouse will be exceeded, and (3) the total shipping cost will be least. Another early problem was the nutrition or diet problem: to choose from among several foods of known cost and nutritional composition a combination of least cost to fulfill certain dietary requirements. Other typical problems include production scheduling for maximum output, and assignment for maximum efficiency of personnel of different abilities to tasks requiring different skills. Several examples are described briefly in Chapter 11 of [7] and there are many in [4], [9], and [22]; see also [1], [2], [4], [6], [13], [14], [18], and [23] for still more examples.

The intimate connection between linear programming and the theory of games is discussed in [20] and [21]; see also the brief statements in [7] Chapter 12, [10] Chapter 5, or [19] Chapter 11.

The word "programming" has acquired a second widely accepted technical meaning—namely, planning and scheduling of numerical calculations, often on a digital computing machine. Since we do not consider this aspect, the reader must look elsewhere (for example, [7] Chapter 9) for suggestions on programming problems in linear programming.

F. A. F.

New York City
April, 1960

Contents

Introduction

The name "linear programming" is given to any method for finding where a given linear function of several variables takes on an extreme value, and what that value is, when the variables are required to be nonnegative and to satisfy further constraints of the form of linear equalities or inequalities. In early applications, very roughly a decade ago, "programming" meant planning or scheduling, and the adjective "linear" referred to the algebraic character of the conditions required of an acceptable plan; the combined term now has the fixed technical meaning just given.

Consider, for example, the problem of maximizing $3x + 4y$ subject to these constraints:

$$x \geq 0, \qquad y \geq 0, \qquad 2x + 5y \leq 10, \qquad \text{and} \qquad 4x + 3y \leq 12.$$

The constraints give rise to a simple configuration in the plane. The coordinates (x, y) of a point will satisfy all the constraints if and only if the point lies in the

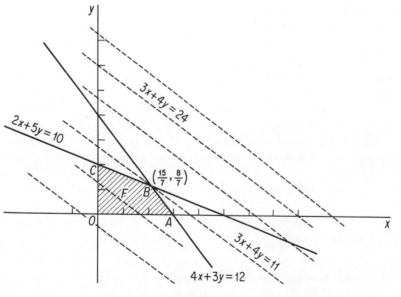

FIGURE 1

set F, consisting of all points inside or on a side of the shaded polygon $OABCO$ (Fig. 1). The level lines (dotted) of the function $3x + 4y$ are parallel to the line

$$3x + 4y = 24,$$

indicating that the desired maximum with a value of 11 will occur at the point B.

Many features of this example are typical of a more general problem in linear programming:

To maximize

$$f = \sum_{j=1}^{n} c_j x_j$$

subject to the constraints

$$x_j \geq 0 \quad (j = 1, \cdots, n) \qquad \text{and} \qquad \sum_{j=1}^{n} a_{\alpha j} x_j \leq b_\alpha \quad (\alpha = 1, \cdots, m).$$

Let us denote by F the set of all points whose coordinates (x_j) satisfy all the constraints. Three basic questions arise.

1. *Consistency*. Are the given constraints consistent? If not, then F is empty and the problem has no solution. If F is not empty then the second question arises.

2. *Boundedness*. Does the given function f take on arbitrarily large values on F? If so, then the problem has no solution. If not, then under the particular conditions of a linear programming problem there is a point P of F that is *optimal* in the sense that if Q is any point of F then $f(Q) \leq f(P)$, and the third question arises.

3. *Location*. How can one find an optimal point?

One general numerical method in linear programming, the simplex method, has come to be preferred except in certain special cases in which special methods may be more effective. Our purpose is to discuss the mathematical theory of the simplex method, leaving entirely aside considerations of arithmetical efficiency.

In fortunate instances, of course, answers to the questions of consistency or boundedness may be evident at the outset. One aim here, however, is to prepare the problem before calculations begin in such a way that favorable answers to those questions are tentatively assumed for the given problem and can be guaranteed for the prepared problem. The calculations themselves then reveal whether or not those assumptions are justified for the given problem. The simplex algorithm terminates automatically, in fact, and full information is then available both on the given problem and on a second closely associated problem called the dual of the given problem.

1.   The Allocation Problem; Duality

We begin with a typical problem in linear programming, which serves also to introduce the important idea of duality. Suppose that materials $\mu(\mu = 1, \cdots, M)$ are available in quantities m_μ, that activities $\alpha(\alpha = 1, \cdots, A)$ are possible, and that one unit of α uses a quantity $q_{\mu\alpha}$ of μ and produces c_α units of a single desired commodity. It is required to determine an allocation $x_\alpha \geq 0$ of the activities α

that will maximize the total output $T = \Sigma\, c_\alpha x_\alpha$ of the desired commodity subject to the availability of materials; that is,

$$\Sigma_\alpha\, q_{\mu\alpha} x_\alpha \leq m_\mu.$$

In the context of the allocation problem, let the price of a unit of material μ, expressed in units of the desired commodity, be denoted by y_μ. The numbers y_μ are sometimes called "accounting prices." If, as we assume, there is no penalty if μ is not used at all in producing the desired commodity then $y_\mu \geq 0$. It seems reasonable also to require that the price of all materials used in a unit of activity α will amount to at least as much as the price c_α of the output:

$$\Sigma_\mu\, y_\mu q_{\mu\alpha} \geq c_\alpha.$$

One may then ask for values of the y_μ, subject to the conditions just mentioned, that yield a minimum total accounting price $P = \Sigma\, y_\mu m_\mu$ of the entire stock m_μ ($u = 1, \cdots, M$). This is a "valuation" problem as contrasted with the allocation problem. (See [4] for details.)

The two problems may be stated explicitly as follows, with m_μ, c_α, and $q_{\mu\alpha}$ given:

Allocation (primal)	Valuation (dual)
Maximize	Minimize
$f(x_1, \cdots, x_A) = \Sigma c_\alpha x_\alpha$	$g(y_1, \cdots, y_M) = \Sigma m_\mu y_\mu$
subject to	subject to
$x_\alpha \geq 0 \quad (\alpha = 1, \cdots, A)$	$y_\mu \geq 0 \quad (\mu = 1, \cdots, M)$
$\Sigma_\alpha\, q_{\mu\alpha} x_\alpha \leq m_\mu \quad (\mu = 1, \cdots, M)$	$\Sigma_\mu\, y_\mu q_{\mu\alpha} \geq c_\alpha \quad (\alpha = 1, \cdots, A).$

The two problems are said to be dual to each other and, as we shall see, an effective solution of either by the simplex method yields simultaneously a solution of the other. For practical reasons one will solve the allocation or the valuation problems according as $M < A$ or $A < M$. The one actually solved is conventionally called the primal problem. Our discussion will deal explicitly with the maximizing problem, and we therefore call it the primal problem.

The problem dual to that of our numerical example is to minimize $10u + 12v$ subject to the constraints

$$u \geq 0, \qquad v \geq 0, \qquad 2u + 4v \geq 3, \qquad \text{and} \qquad 5u + 3v \geq 4.$$

The required minimum, attained for $u = \frac{1}{2}$, $v = \frac{1}{2}$, is again 11.

2. Matrix Notation for Dual Problems

In the numerical example it turned out that, under the various constraints,

$$\max\,(3x + 4y) = 11 = \min\,(10u + 12v).$$

This special result is not accidental. In order to give a setting for the general result, it is convenient to introduce matrix notation.

Let us agree, to begin with, on the meaning of inequalities involving an indexed set $S = (s_k)$ in which the index may have more than one value. Define:

$$S \geq 0 \quad \text{if} \quad s_k \geq 0 \quad \text{for all values of } k,$$
$$S \geq 0 \quad \text{if} \quad S \geq 0 \quad \text{and} \quad s_k > 0 \quad \text{for some value of } k,$$
and $\quad S > 0 \quad \text{if} \quad s_k > 0 \quad \text{for all values of } k.$

The definitions are similar if each element of S has several indices. We agree, moreover, that $S \geq T$ (etc.) means $S - T \geq 0$ (etc.).

The respective inequalities are clearly preserved under addition, and may even become stronger. If S and T are matrices such that $S > 0$ and $T > 0$ then clearly $ST > 0$; but $S > 0$ and $T \geq 0$ imply only $ST \geq 0$ although, of course, it may happen that in fact $ST > 0$; any weaker hypotheses will imply only $ST \geq 0$.

The constraints in a linear programming problem were described as linear equations or inequalities. It is sometimes advantageous to replace some constraints by equivalent constraints of a desired form. For example, an equation $a = b$ may be replaced by the inequality $a \leq b$ and either of the inequalities $a \geq b$ or $-b \geq -a$. Similarly, the inequality $c \geq d$ may be replaced, if desired, by the equation $c - e = d$ and the inequality $e \geq 0$.

By appropriate adjustments in the constraints, if necessary, we may therefore formulate the general problem of linear programming and its dual as follows:

Primal	Dual
Maximize	Minimize

$$f(x_1, \cdots, x_n) = \sum_{j=1}^{n} c_j x_j \qquad\qquad g(u_1, \cdots, u_m) = \sum_{\alpha=1}^{m} u_\alpha b_\alpha$$

subject to $\qquad\qquad\qquad\qquad\qquad$ subject to

$$x_j \geq 0 \quad (j = 1, \cdots, n) \qquad\qquad u_\alpha \geq 0 \quad (\alpha = 1, \cdots, m) \quad (2.1)$$

$$\sum_{j=1}^{n} a_{\alpha j} x_j \leq b_\alpha \quad (\alpha = 1, \cdots, m) \qquad \sum_{\alpha=1}^{m} u_\alpha a_{\alpha j} \geq c_j \quad (j = 1, \cdots, n).$$

With $\alpha = 1, \cdots, m$ and $j = 1, \cdots, n$, introduce the matrix $A = [a_{\alpha j}]$, row vectors $C = [c_j]$ and $U = [u_\alpha]$, and column vectors $B = [b_\alpha]^t$ and $X = [x_j]^t$. Our problems may then be stated as follows:

Primal	Dual
Maximize	Minimize

$$f(X) = CX \qquad\qquad\qquad g(U) - UB \qquad (2.2)$$

subject to $\qquad\qquad\qquad\qquad\qquad$ subject to

$$X \geq 0, \quad AX \leq B \qquad\qquad U \geq 0, \quad UA \geq C.$$

Many authors give also a concise tabular formulation not needed here. It may be mentioned that f is sometimes called the *objective* function or functional.

That max $(3x + 4y) = $ min $(10u + 12v)$ in the numerical example is a special instance of the general fact that if either max CX or min UB exists then they both exist and are equal. We proceed to develop the ideas underlying this fact.

3. Feasibility; Theorems on Duality and Existence

Using the notation of the matrix formulation just given, let us say that the (primal) constraints are consistent, or that A and B are consistent, if the constraining inequalities $X \geq 0$ and $AX \leq B$ are consistent (have a solution). Let us describe as *feasible* a point or vector X satisfying all these constraints, and denote by F the set of feasible points. Let us also say that the dual constraints are consistent, or that A and C are consistent, if the inequalities $U \geq 0$ and $UA \geq C$ are consistent, and call a point or vector U *feasible* if it satisfies these conditions. Mention of a feasible vector will imply consistency of the appropriate constraints.

Examples.   1. A and C consistent ($U = (0,0)$ feasible) but A and B inconsistent:

$$A = \begin{bmatrix} 2 & 3 \\ 1 & 1 \end{bmatrix}, \qquad B = [2, -1]^t, \qquad C = [0, 0].$$

2. Both A and C inconsistent and A and B inconsistent:

$$A = \begin{bmatrix} 0 & 1 \\ 0 & 2 \end{bmatrix}, \qquad B = [-1, 2]^t, \qquad C = [1, -1].$$

A feasible vector X is *optimal* if $CY \leq CX$ for all feasible vectors Y; that is, CX is *maximal*. A feasible vector U is *optimal* if $VB \geq UB$ for all feasible V; that is UB is *minimal*.

If X and U are feasible then the constraints yield the inequalities $CX \leq UAX \leq UB$, whence $CX \leq UB$. Now suppose that $\overline{X}$ and $\overline{U}$ are feasible and that $C\overline{X} = \overline{U}B$. If Y is feasible then $CY \leq \overline{U}B = C\overline{X}$, whence $\overline{X}$ is optimal. In a precisely similar way, $\overline{U}$ is optimal.

The DUALITY THEOREM asserts that the sufficient condition just given is also necessary: *A feasible* X *(or* U*) is optimal if and only if there exists a feasible* U *(or* X*) such that* UB $=$ CX. A further fundamental result is this EXISTENCE THEOREM: *In order that one problem of a dual pair, and hence both, may have optimal vectors, it is necessary and sufficient that both* A *and* B *be consistent and* A *and* C *be consistent; in other words, that both the primal and the dual constraints be consistent. In the favorable case,* finally, *max* CX $=$ *min* UB.

Simple illustrations of these ideas may be found in our original numerical example. The vectors $(x,y) = (1,1)$ and $(u,v) = (1,1)$ are both feasible. Since both systems of constraints are consistent, we know that both problems have optimal vectors. Suppose that we have learned, perhaps from the diagram of

Fig. 1, that $(\frac{15}{7}, \frac{8}{7})$ is an optimal vector for the primal problem. We are able to conclude that a feasible vector (u,v) will be optimal if and only if $10u + 12v = 11$. In this instance the optimal vector may be found immediately by combining this equation with the given constraints.

Proofs of the theorems on duality and existence are by no means trivial. Following the thorough treatment in [12] (papers 1 and 4), we outline the proofs later in Appendix II; see also [19] Sec. 11.5 and [7] Chap. 5. The proofs are constructive in that they indicate calculations that settle the questions of feasibility and boundedness and produce an optimal vector when one exists. As pointed out at the end of Appendix II, however, it is usually more advantageous to obtain the same practical results by the simplex method. That method becomes more intelligible in the light of certain properties of convex sets.

4.   Convex Sets; Boundedness

A subset S of a linear space is said to be *convex* if $P \in S$ and $Q \in S$ imply that $(1 - t)P + tQ \in S$ for $0 \le t \le 1$; that is, if P and Q are elements of S then so is every point of the line segment joining them. (See Fig. 2.) On referring

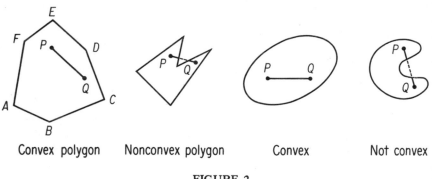

Convex polygon   Nonconvex polygon   Convex   Not convex

FIGURE 2

to the diagram (Fig. 1) for the numerical example, one observes that the feasible points constitute a convex polygonal region and that the optimal point is not interior to the region, but lies on its boundary. This situation is typical.

Let $h(x) = \Sigma_j\, a_j x_j$. The solutions of the linear equation $h(x) = b$ form a hyperplane. The solutions of the linear inequality $h(x) < b$ (or $> b$) consist of all points on one side (or the other) of the bounding hyperplane $h(x) = b$. (See Fig. 3.) The solutions of the linear inequality $h(x) \le b$ (or $\ge b$) consist of all points on the bounding hyperplane ($=$) or on one side ($<$) (or the other, $>$) of it. The set of all points satisfying a linear inequality is called a *half-space*, and the half-space is said to be *closed* or *open* according as the bounding hyperplane is included ($\le$ or $\ge$) or is not included ($<$ or $>$). In

Fig. 3 the open half-space $3x + 2y > 6$ is shaded. One may easily verify that the set of solutions of any linear equation or inequality is a convex set.

Observe next that the intersection of any class of convex sets is convex. The set F of all feasible points of the (primal) linear programming problem (2.1) or (2.2) consists of the intersection of a finite number of closed half-spaces; F is therefore a convex set.

Our first problem is to learn whether the constraints are inconsistent, so that F is empty, or consistent, so that F is not empty. It will be possible later to discuss this consistency question in rather simple terms; meanwhile, we *assume* that F is not empty.

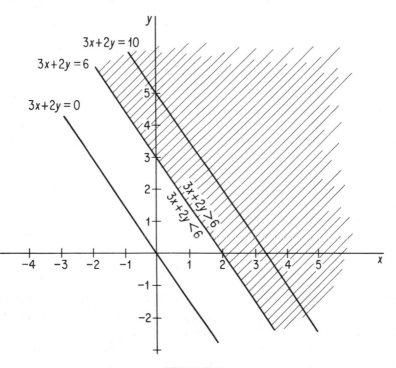

FIGURE 3

If F consists of a single point there is no genuine competition and no need of special calculation. We therefore assume that F has at least two points and hence, being convex, infinitely many. If f is constant on F then every point of F is already an optimal point and the problem is trivial. We therefore assume that f is not constant on F.

Is there necessarily an optimal point among the feasible points F? In the plane, consider the constraints

$$x \geq 0, \qquad y \geq 0, \qquad \text{and} \qquad y \leq 1.$$

The set F (shaded in Fig. 4) consists of the strip $x \geq 0$, $0 \leq y \leq 1$. If the linear function $f(x,y)$ is simply x, then f can take on arbitrarily large values and no optimal point exists. If $f(x,y) = -x$, however, then $f(x,y) \leq 0$ on F, $\max f = 0$, and all the points $(0,y)$ $(0 \leq y \leq 1)$ are optimal points.

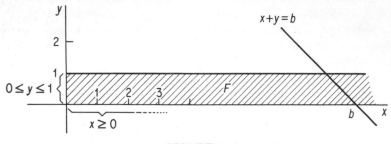

FIGURE 4

It is helpful at this stage to introduce the idea of boundedness. A set of points in the Euclidean linear space we are using is said to be *bounded* if it is contained in some sphere, or in a box such as $|x_i| \leq p_i$ $(i = 1, \cdots, n)$. The strip F of the preceding paragraph is not bounded, nor (in this sense of the word) is a hyperplane or a half-space, but the set F of the numerical example is bounded. Similarly, a real-valued function g defined for X in a set S is said to be *bounded above* on S if there is a (finite) number K, independent of X, such that X in S implies $g(X) \leq K$; then K is said to be an *upper bound* for g on S.

Suppose now that the set F of feasible points is bounded. There is a theorem of mathematical analysis that uses further properties of F and f (technically, F is closed and f is continuous) to conclude that f is bounded above on F, and that if F is not empty then there is a point of F at which f takes on its largest value—that is, an optimal point.

If F is not bounded, then, since f is not constant on F, f may or (as $f = x$ in the example just given) may not be bounded above on F. If f is bounded above on F, then, as we shall see, F has an optimal point.

It may be noted in passing that the necessary existence of an optimal point depends on the special character of F as the intersection of a finite number of closed half-spaces. For example, for each fixed positive value of t the points (x,y) satisfying the linear inequality $t^2y - x \geq 2t$ constitute the closed half-space of all points lying on the line $t^2y - x = 2t$ or above and to the left of it. The intersection E (shaded in Fig. 5) of all these half-spaces (infinitely many, one for each $t > 0$) is readily seen to consist of those points satisfying both the linear inequality $x \leq 0$ and the nonlinear inequality $xy \leq -1$. Let f be the linear functional $f(x,y) = x$. It is evident that $f(x,y) \leq 0$ at each point of E, and that zero is the best possible upper bound of f on E in the sense that no negative number is an upper bound. At the same time, there is no point (x,y) of E such that $f(x,y) = 0$; there is no optimal point.

If it is not evident from the constraints (or perhaps from compelling intuitive considerations) that F is bounded, one may adjoin a condition

$$\sum_{j=1}^{n} x_j \leq b_{m+1}$$

with $b_{m+1} > 0$ and "large." It is never necessary in practice to assign a value to b_{m+1}. The set G of feasible points of the augmented system of constraints

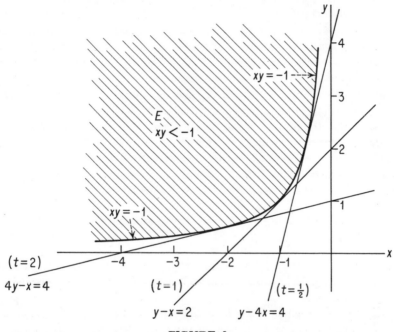

FIGURE 5

is certainly contained in F. Moreover, G is bounded, for

$$0 \leq x_j \leq b_{m+1} \qquad (j = 1, \cdots, n).$$

Without appealing to the theorem cited above, we may go on to conclude that f is bounded above on G because

$$f(X) \leq b_{m+1} \sum_{j=1}^{n} |c_j|.$$

The dual problem, moreover, is now to minimize

$$\sum_{\alpha=1}^{m} u_\alpha b_\alpha + u_{m+1} b_{m+1}$$

subject to

$$u_\alpha \geq 0, \qquad u_{m+1} \geq 0,$$

and

$$\sum_\alpha u_\alpha a_{\alpha j} + u_{m+1} \geq c_j \qquad (j = 1, \cdots, n).$$

It is clear that all these constraints are met by choosing

$$u_\alpha = 0 \quad (\alpha = 1, \cdots, m) \qquad \text{and} \qquad u_{m+1} = \max_j |c_j|.$$

Thus the dual constraints are consistent and we conclude this time from the Existence Theorem of Section 3—since we are assuming that the primal constraints are consistent—that the primal problem has an optimal vector (and so does the dual).

If there occurs in G an optimal vector X not depending on b_{m+1}, then X will be an optimal vector of the original problem.

If every optimal vector in G depends on b_{m+1}, and if this is true no matter how large b_{m+1} may be, we must conclude both that F is unbounded and that f is not bounded above on F. It will then not make any sense to try to maximize f without imposing some further constraint—based preferably on practical considerations—which has the effect, like the rather artificial constraint just used, of excluding all but a bounded subset of F.

Suppose that the problem were to maximize $f(x,y) = x$ on the set F:$0 \le x$, $0 \le y \le 1$. One would adjoin the constraint $x + y \le b$, find the maximum $f(b,0) = b$, and conclude that f is not bounded above on F. (See Fig. 4.)

We shall *assume* henceforth that *the set* F *of feasible points is bounded;* for convenience, in fact, we assume that the mth constraint is

$$\sum_{j=1}^{n} x_j \le b_m,$$

with $b_m > 0$ and "large." It follows that *if the primal constraints* (including this mth constraint) *are consistent, so that* F *is not empty, then the primal problem has an optimal vector.*

In the present situation F is a bounded convex set consisting of the intersection of a finite number of closed half-spaces. Since the level surfaces of the linear objective function f are hyperplanes, the set O of optimal points is a convex set consisting, as we shall see, of the intersection of F with the hyperplane $f(X) = c$ for some value of c. Since c must be as large as possible, O cannot contain interior points of F and must therefore be a face (of dimension less than n), or edge, or vertex of F.

The name "simplex method" may stem from the fact that the points having

$$x_j \ge 0 \quad (j = 1, \cdots, n) \qquad \text{and} \qquad \Sigma_j x_j \le b \quad (\text{with } b > 0)$$

constitute a simplex as that term is defined in combinatorial topology.

The next step is to introduce an auxiliary problem, here called the prepared problem (P). The problem (P) will have constraints that are clearly consistent. The set F_P of feasible points of (P) may be unbounded, but the function to be maximized will be bounded above on F_P. The simplex method will yield an optimal point for problem (P) and will settle the consistency and boundedness questions for the original problem. In any favorable case, moreover, the optimal point for (P) will yield an optimal point for the original problem (and one for the dual problem will be evident from the final calculations). For motivation see, for example, [7], [2] part I, and [4].

5. The Prepared Problem; Boundedness and Consistency

For present purposes let us denote the column vector $[x_j]^t$ $(j = 1, \cdots, n)$ by x, and the row vector $[c_j]$ $(j = 1, \cdots, n)$ by c. The problem has arisen. let us suppose, of maximizing

$$f(x) = \sum_{j=1}^{n} c_j x_j = cx$$

subject to the constraints

$$x_j \geq 0 \qquad (j = 1, \cdots, n)$$

and m further linear constraints of the form

$$(h_\alpha) \qquad \sum_{j=1}^{n} a_{\alpha j} x_j *_\alpha b_\alpha \qquad (\alpha = 1, \cdots, m),$$

where $*_\alpha$ may be $\geq$, $=$, or $\leq$.

As a first step, if any $b_\alpha < 0$ then (h_α) is to be multiplied by -1; henceforth $b_\alpha \geq 0$ $(\alpha = 1, \cdots, m)$.

The further treatment of (h_α) depends on the relation $*_\alpha$. In order to systematize the notation, once and for all, we rearrange the constraints (h_α) so that those $(g$ in number) in which $*_\alpha$ is "$\geq$" come first, those $(e$ in number) in which $*_\alpha$ is "$=$" come next, and those $(l = m - g - e$ in number) in which $*_\alpha$ is "$\leq$" come last. The order within the group is unimportant. Thus

$*_\alpha$	is	$\geq$	for	$\alpha = 1, \cdots, g;$
$*_\alpha$	is	$=$	for	$\alpha = g + 1, \cdots, g + e;$
$*_\alpha$	is	$\leq$	for	$\alpha = g + e + 1, \cdots, g + e + l = m.$

We wish next to introduce $m + g$ further variables, with associated constraints and associated coefficients for use in f. It is convenient to bring in m of these new variables with indices $1, \cdots, m$; we therefore first replace j by $j + m$, getting a function

$$f(x) = \sum_{j=m+1}^{m+n} c_j x_j$$

and constraints

$$(h_x) \qquad \sum_{j=m+1}^{m+n} a_{\alpha j} x_j *_\alpha b_\alpha \qquad (\alpha = 1, \cdots, m).$$

(The remaining g new variables will have indices $m + n + 1, \cdots, m + n + g$.)

Let us call the problem as it now stands, after these minor adjustments, the *original problem* and refer to it as problem (p). Thus problem (p) is this:
Maximize

$$f(x) = \sum_{j=m+1}^{m+n} c_j x_j$$

subject to   (5.1) Problem (p)

$$x_j \geq 0 \qquad \text{and} \qquad (h_\alpha) \quad \sum_{j=m+1}^{m+n} a_{\alpha j} x_j *_\alpha b_\alpha \qquad (\alpha = 1, \cdots, m).$$

We are now ready to go over to the prepared problem. For $\alpha = 1, \cdots, g$ replace (h_α) by

$$(H_\alpha) \qquad x_\alpha + \sum_{j=m+1}^{m+n} a_{\alpha j} x_j - x_{m+n+\alpha} = b_\alpha,$$

define $c_\alpha = -M$ ($M > 0$ and "large") and $c_{m+n+\alpha} = 0$, and adjoin the constraints $x_\alpha \geq 0$ and $x_{m+n+\alpha} \geq 0$.
    For $\alpha = g + 1, \cdots, g + e$ replace (h_α) by

$$(H_\alpha) \qquad x_\alpha + \sum_{j=m+1}^{m+n} a_{\alpha j} x_j = b_\alpha,$$

define $c_\alpha = -M$ ($M > 0$ and "large"), and adjoin the constraint $x_\alpha \geq 0$.
    For $\alpha = g + e + 1, \cdots, m$ replace (h_α) by

$$(H_\alpha) \qquad x_\alpha + \sum_{j=m+1}^{m+n} a_{\alpha j} x_j = b_\alpha,$$

define $c_\alpha = 0$, and adjoin the constraint $x_\alpha \geq 0$.
    Let us agree to let the index J run from 1 to $N = m + n + g$ (or over a timely subset of that range), put $X = [x_J]^t$, and keep j for the range $m + 1$, $\cdots, m + n$. The new function to be maximized is

$$f(X) = \sum_{J=1}^{N} c_J x_J.$$

In point of fact,

$$f(X) = -M \sum_{\alpha=1}^{g+e} x_\alpha + \sum_{j=m+1}^{m+n} c_j x_j,$$

for all other coefficients are zero. Thus the variables x_J for

$$J = g + e + 1, \cdots, m, m + n + 1, \cdots, N$$

can make no contribution to f. They are called *slack* variables because they "take up the slack" permitted by the inequalities $\leq$ and $\geq$ in (h_α). At the same time, any variable x_α for $\alpha = 1, \cdots, g + e$ whose value is not zero gives rise to a numerically large negative term, $-Mx_\alpha$, and such a term will presumably keep $f(X)$ less than it would be with that $x_\alpha = 0$. The effect of the coefficients

$c_\alpha = -\,M$ for $\alpha = 1, \cdots, g + e$ is therefore to make it rather likely that any optimal vector will have $x_\alpha = 0$ for $\alpha = 1, \cdots, g + e$. These variables are called *artificial* variables. For economic interpretations see [2] (first half) and [4]. It will become clear that the constraints of the original problem are consistent if and only if for one optimal vector of the prepared problem (and hence for all) each artificial variable has the value zero.

The prepared problem, denoted by (P), is this:

Maximize

$$f(X) = \sum_{J=1}^{N} c_J x_J$$

subject to

$$x_J \geq 0$$

(5.2) Problem (P)

and

$$(H_\alpha) \qquad \sum_{J=1}^{N} a_{\alpha J} x_J = b_\alpha \qquad (\alpha = 1, \cdots, m).$$

Here

$$b_\alpha \geq 0, \qquad a_{\alpha\beta} = \delta_{\alpha\beta} \qquad (\beta = 1, \cdots, m),$$

$$a_{\alpha\,m+n+\beta} = -\,\delta_{\alpha\beta} \qquad (\beta = 1, \cdots, g),$$

and $a_{\alpha j}$ come from (h_α). An example is given at the end of our discussion; another is in Section 7.

One advantage of this prepared problem is that *the set F_P of its feasible points is not empty*. Since $b_\alpha \geq 0$ $(\alpha = 1, \cdots, m)$, all the constraints are clearly satisfied by

$$x_J = b_J \qquad (J = 1, \cdots, m) \qquad \text{and} \qquad x_J = 0 \qquad (J = m + 1, \cdots, N).$$

Another feature of problem (P) is that $f(X)$ *is bounded above on F_P*. Since $x_J \geq 0$ on F_P for each value of J, the first sum on the right in

$$f(X) = -\,M \sum_{\alpha=1}^{g+e} x_\alpha + \sum_{j=m+1}^{m+n} c_j x_j$$

cannot be positive and therefore

$$f(X) \leq \sum_{j=m+1}^{m+n} c_j x_j.$$

Now the mth constraint is

$$x_m + \Sigma_j x_j \leq b_m,$$

whence

$$0 \leq x_J \leq b_m \qquad (J = m, m + 1, \ldots, m + n),$$

and it follows as claimed that

$$f(X) \leq b_m \Sigma_j \mid c_j \mid,$$

where the right-hand member of the inequality does not depend on X.

There is this apparent difficulty with problem (P), however, that F_P *may be unbounded.* If, for example, the first constraint in problem (p) is

$$\Sigma_j\, a_{1j}x_j \geq b_1 \ (\geq 0)$$

then the first constraint in problem (P) is

$$x_1 + \Sigma_j\, a_{1j}x_j - x_{m+n+1} = b_1.$$

Then if $t \geq 0$ and the vector $X(t)$ is defined to be

$$X(t) = (b_1 + t,\, b_2,\, \cdots,\, b_m,\, 0,\, \cdots,\, 0,\, t,\, 0,\, \cdots,\, 0)$$

where

$$x_{m+n+1} = t,$$

then $X(t)$ is feasible and it follows, since t can have arbitrarily large values, that F_P is unbounded.

The example given in Section 4 shows that it is by no means evident a priori that problem (P) has an optimal vector. It is accordingly of critical importance to show, as we shall later on, that the simplex method necessarily delivers an optimal vector for problem (P). We proceed now to develop those relationships between problems (p) and (P) which underlie the interpretation of the results of the simplex calculation.

Let us say that a vector X that is feasible for problem (P) is an *indicative* vector if every artificial variable has the value zero: $x_\alpha = 0$ $(\alpha = 1,\, \cdots,\, g + e)$. We first prove

Lemma 1: *Problem* (p) *has feasible points* (its constraints are consistent) *if and only if problem* (P) *has an indicative vector.*

This result can be seen most easily, perhaps, when the constraints (H_α) of problem (P) are written out explicitly. From (5.2) we have:

$$x_1 \qquad\qquad + \sum_{j=m+1}^{m+n} a_{1j}x_j \qquad - x_{m+n+1} \qquad\qquad = b_1$$

$$\cdots\cdots\cdots\cdots$$

$$x_g \qquad\qquad + \sum_{j=m+1}^{m+n} a_{gj}x_j \qquad\qquad - x_{m+n+g} = b_g$$

$$x_{g+1} \qquad + \sum_{j=m+1}^{m+n} a_{g+1\ j}x_j \qquad\qquad = b_{g+1}$$

$$\cdots\cdots\cdots\cdots\cdots\cdots \qquad (5.3)$$

$$x_{g+e} \qquad + \sum_{j=m+1}^{m+n} a_{g+e\ j}x_j \qquad\qquad = b_{g+e}$$

$$x_{g+e+1} + \sum_{j=m+1}^{m+n} a_{g+e+1\ j}x_j \qquad\qquad = b_{g+e+1}$$

$$\cdots\cdots\cdots\cdots\cdots\cdots$$

$$x_m \qquad + \sum_{j=m+1}^{m+n} a_{mj}x_j \qquad\qquad = b_m$$

A vector $X \epsilon E_N$ is feasible if $X \geq 0$ and X satisfies equations (5.3). If X is also indicative then

$$x_\alpha = 0 \qquad (\alpha = 1, \cdots, g + e).$$

But then the vector

$$y = [x_j]^t \qquad (j = m + 1, \cdots, m + n)$$

is ≥ 0 and satisfies (5.3). It follows from these equations and from the fact that

$$x_J \geq 0 \qquad (J = g + e + 1, \cdots, m, \; m + n + 1, \cdots, m + n + g)$$

that y satisfies the constraints (h_α) of (5.1) for $\alpha = 1, \cdots, m$. Hence y is a feasible vector for problem (p).

Vice versa, if $y = [y_j]^t$ is ≥ 0 and satisfies the constraints (h_α) of (5.1), then in (5.3) we set

$$x_J = y_J \qquad (J = j = m + 1, \cdots, m + n)$$

and set

$$x_J = 0 \qquad (J = 1, \cdots, g + e);$$

and we use equations (5.3) for $\alpha = 1, \cdots, g$ to define $x_{m+n+1}, \cdots, x_{m+n+g}$, and equations (5.3) for $\alpha = g + e + 1, \cdots, m$ to define $x_{g+e+1}, \cdots, x_m$. Then $X = [x_j]^t$ clearly satisfies (5.3). It follows from (5.1) and (5.3) that $X \geq 0$. Finally, X is indicative because

$$x_J = 0 \qquad (J = 1, \cdots, g + e),$$

and Lemma 1 is proved.

The construction in the preceding paragraph enables us to associate with each $x \epsilon F_p$ a unique indicative $X \epsilon F_P$; we shall denote this particular X by $X(x)$. Similarly, for $X \epsilon E_N$ we define $x(X) \epsilon E_n$ to be $x = [x_j]^t$ with x_j for $j = m + 1, \cdots, m + n$ precisely the respective components of X. Clearly $x(X(x)) = x$ for each $x \epsilon F_p$, and if X is indicative then $X(x(X)) = X$.

With these definitions in mind we may state an immediate *corollary of Lemma 1*: If X is an indicative feasible vector for problem (P) then $x(X) \epsilon F_p$; if $x \epsilon F_p$ then $X(x) \epsilon F_P$ and is indicative.

The values of the functional

$$f(X) = \Sigma_J c_J x_J$$

for problem (P) and those of

$$f(x) = \sum_{j=m+1}^{m+n} c_j x_j$$

for problem (p) are closely related:

$$f(X) = - M \sum_{\alpha - 1}^{g+e} x_\alpha + \Sigma_j c_j x_j = - M \sum_{\alpha - 1}^{g+e} x_\alpha + f(x(X)).$$

If X is indicative then

$$f(X) = f(x(X));$$

if $x \epsilon F_p$ then $X(x)$ is indicative and

$$f(x) = f(X(x)).$$

Lemma 2. *If problem* (P) *has an indicative vector* X *and an optimal vector* Y *then* Y *is indicative.*

If Y is not indicative then $y_\alpha > 0$ for some value of α in the range $1, \cdots, g + e$. It follows that if M is sufficiently large then

$$f(X) - f(Y) = + M \Sigma_\alpha y_\alpha + f(x(X)) - f(x(Y)) > 0,$$

contradicting the optimality of Y; this proves the lemma.

It follows at once that if problem (P) has an indicative vector then every optimal vector (if any) of problem (P) is indicative. The simplex method produces an optimal vector Y of problem (P), and the consistency question for problem (p) is then settled: *The constraints of problem* (p) *are consistent if and only if each optimal vector* Y *for problem* (P) *is indicative.*

The relation between optimal vectors $\bar{x}$ for problem (p) and optimal vectors $\overline{X}$ for problem (P) is now easy to see.

Lemma 3. *If* $\bar{x}$ *is an optimal vector for problem* (p) *then* $X(\bar{x})$ *is an* (indicative) *optimal vector for problem* (P); *if* $\overline{X}$ *is an indicative optimal vector for problem* (P) *then* $x(\overline{X})$ *is an optimal vector for problem* (p).

Suppose first that $\bar{x}$ were optimal for (p) and that $X(\bar{x})$, which is indicative, were not optimal for (P). Then there would exist, by Lemma 2, an indicative $Y \in F_P$ such that

$$f(X(\bar{x})) < f(Y).$$

But then

$$x(Y) \in F_p \qquad \text{and} \qquad f(\bar{x}) = f(X(\bar{x})) < f(Y) = f(x(Y)),$$

contradicting the optimality of $\bar{x}$. Vice versa, if $\overline{X}$ were an indicative optimal vector for (P) and $x(\overline{X})$ were not optimal for (p) then there would exist a vector $y \in F_p$ such that

$$f(x(\overline{X})) < f(y).$$

But then

$$X(y) \in F_P$$

and is indicative, and

$$f(\overline{X}) = f(x(\overline{X})) < f(y) = f(X(y)),$$

contradicting the optimality of $\overline{X}$.

We are now able to interpret in all cases the result of the calculation that generates an optimal vector Y for problem (P). If Y is not indicative then the constraints of problem (p) are inconsistent and the set F_p of its feasible points is empty. If Y is indicative then F_p is not empty and $x(Y)$ is an optimal point for problem (p). If $x(Y)$ involves the "bounding parameter" b_m, no matter how large b_m may be, then F_p is unbounded and f is unbounded on F_p. If $x(Y)$ does not involve b_m, when b_m is sufficiently large, then the bounding constraint $\Sigma_j x_j \leq b_m$ was unnecessary; F_p is bounded and any $x(Y)$ expressible without use of b_m will be an optimal vector for problem (p) with the bounding constraint omitted.

The specific steps of the simplex method are motivated by the particular character of the convex set F_P of feasible points for problem (P).

6.   Optimal Points; Motivation of the Simplex Method

Let us consider for a moment the (hyper-) planes π_d having an equation $f(X) = d$ for some value of d. We know that the convex set F_P is not empty. If Y is a particular feasible point, and we choose $d = f(Y)$, then the intersection of π_d and F_P clearly contains Y and is therefore not empty. At the same time, since $f(X)$ is bounded above on F_P, π_d will not intersect F_P if d is larger than some upper bound for f on F_P.

It follows from a theorem of mathematical analysis (see Appendix I, [1] Chap. IV, sec. 3, Th. 1) that f has on F_P a *least* upper bound $\bar{d}$; this means that $\bar{d}$ is an upper bound and that if $d < \bar{d}$ then d is not an upper bound for f on F_P. If Y is a feasible point that is not optimal then $f(Y) < \bar{d}$ and π_d will intersect F_P if $f(Y) \leq d < \bar{d}$. On the other hand, if $d > \bar{d}$ then π_d will not intersect F_P.

What about the plane $\pi_{\bar{d}}$ with equation $f(X) = \bar{d}$? We claim that X is an optimal vector for problem (P) if and only if X lies in the intersection G of $\pi_{\bar{d}}$ and F_P. If $X \epsilon G$ then $X \epsilon F_P$, and if Y is feasible then $f(Y) \leq \bar{d} = f(X)$; hence X is optimal. On the other hand, if X is feasible then $X \epsilon F_P$ and $f(X) \leq \bar{d}$. If X were optimal and had $f(X) < \bar{d}$ then there would exist a feasible Y with $f(X) < f(Y)$, and X would not be optimal; hence $f(X) = \bar{d}$. Thus the set of optimal points for problem (P) coincides with the intersection G of $\pi_{\bar{d}}$ and F_P, and the existence of an optimal point will be established if we demonstrate that G is not empty.

When F_P is bounded it is intuitively evident and easy to show that G is not empty. When F_P is unbounded we shall have to appeal, as noted in Section 4, to the fact that F_P is the intersection of a finite number of closed half-spaces. It is highly plausible—indeed true—that the linear and finite character of our programming problem excludes the possibility of "tangency at infinity" such as that of the example in Section 4. Our general proof that F_P has an optimal point, while rather lengthy, uses only the ideas already available to us, along with the notion of an extreme point of a convex set.

A point X of a convex set S is said to be an *extreme point* or *vector* of S if there do not exist distinct vectors Y and Z of S such that

$$X = \frac{Y + Z}{2};$$

briefly, X is not between two other points of S. The extreme points of a plane convex polygon, or of a cube, or of a tetrahedron are its vertices. The extreme points of F in Fig. 1 (p. 1) are O, A, B, and C; those of the convex polygon

Fig. 2 (p. 6) are A, B, C, D, E, and F. The extreme points of a circular disc are on its circumference; those of a solid sphere are on its surface. The extreme points of the plane strip $0 \leq x < \infty$, $0 \leq y \leq 1$ are the points $(0,0)$ and $(0,1)$. It is plausible and true (we omit the proof) that extreme points, and only extreme points, can be deleted from a convex set without destroying its convexity.

In order to deal effectively with extreme points we develop a second characterization. A point X is feasible if $X \geq 0$ and $AX = B$. For $J = 1, \cdots, N$ let A_J denote the Jth column vector of the matrix $[a_{\alpha J}]$. In the expression

$$B = \Sigma_J A_J x_J$$

let us say that the indices J, the variables x_J, and the vectors A_J for which $x_J > 0$ are *active* indices, variables, and vectors, and let us denote by Q_X the set of active indices J. We show now that X *is an extreme point of* F_P *if and only if the set of active vectors* A_J ($J \in Q_X$) *is independent*.

Suppose first that X is not an extreme point of F_P. Then there exist distinct vectors Y and Z in F_P such that

$$X = \frac{Y + Z}{2}.$$

Now $B = AY = AZ$, and every index in either Q_Y or Q_Z is in Q_X, for if either $y_J > 0$ or $z_J > 0$ then

$$x_J = \frac{y_J + z_J}{2} > 0.$$

At the same time, the set of those vectors A_J such that J belongs either to Q_Y or to Q_Z (or both) must be a dependent set, for $A(Y - Z) = 0$ with $Y \neq Z$. Hence the active vectors A_J ($J \in Q_X$) are dependent.

Suppose conversely that the active vectors A_J ($J \in Q_X$) are dependent. Then there exist constants w_J ($J \in Q_X$), not all zero, such that

$$AW = \Sigma A_J w_J = 0 \qquad (J \in Q_X).$$

Since the last relation is homogeneous, we can multiply W by a nonzero number, if necessary, to assure that

$$0 \leq |w_J| < x_J \qquad (J \in Q_X).$$

Then $Y = X + W$ and $Z = X - W$ are both feasible. Since $Y \neq Z$ and $X = (Y + Z)/2$, X is not an extreme point of F_P. The proposed characterization of extreme points is therefore established.

Let E denote the set of extreme vectors of F_P. In problem (P),

$$B = \sum_{\alpha=1}^{m} A_\alpha b_\alpha$$

and the vectors A_α ($\alpha = 1, \cdots, m$) are independent. The vector $X = [x_J]^t$ with $x_J = b_J$ ($J = 1, \cdots, m$) and $x_J = 0$ otherwise is therefore an extreme vector of F_P, and the set E is not empty.

The set E, moreover, is finite. An independent set of m-component column vectors cannot contain more than m vectors, and there are consequently at most

$$N! \sum_{k=1}^{m} [k!(N-k)!]^{-1}$$

independent subsets of the set A_J ($J = 1, \cdots, N$). An independent subset will yield an extreme vector if and only if there exist constants $x_J \geq 0$ such that

$$B = \Sigma A_J x_J$$

and the numbers x_J, when they exist, are unique. *The number of extreme vectors of* F_P *is* therefore *finite*.

Let e denote the number of extreme vectors of F_P, let X_h ($h = 1, \cdots, e$) denote the extreme vectors, and let C denote the row vector $[c_J]$ ($J = 1, \cdots, N$). Among the finite set of numbers $f(X_h) = CX_h$ ($h = 1, \cdots, e$) there is a greatest. We say that an extreme vector X is a *maximal* extreme vector if

$$CX_h \leq CX \qquad (h = 1, \cdots, e).$$

Let $\overline{X}$ denote a maximal extreme vector.

The argument used recently to prove that if the active vectors A_J are dependent then X is not an extreme point can easily be adapted to show that *if* F_P has an optimal vector *then* $\overline{X}$ is an optimal vector. Although this is not enough by itself to justify the conclusion that F_P has an optimal vector, it suggests that the existence of an optimal vector could be established by showing directly that $\overline{X}$ *is an optimal vector of* F_P. This we do by elaborating the above argument so as to exploit the fact that f is bounded above on F_P.

We first develop a criterion of optimality. Suppose that X and Y are both feasible. Then the equations $B = AX = AY$ imply that $A(X - Y) = 0$; in other words, the difference $Z = X - Y$ satisfies the homogeneous equation $AZ = 0$. Conversely, if Y is feasible then $Y + Z$ is feasible if $AZ = 0$ and $Y + Z \geq 0$; and if Y is feasible then these two conditions together are also necessary for the feasibility of $Y + Z$. Now a feasible X is optimal if and only if $CW \leq CX$ for every feasible W. It follows that X *is optimal if and only if the two relations* $X + Y \geq 0$ *and* $AY = 0$ *together imply that* $CY \leq 0$; the two relations imply that $X + Y$ is feasible, and $C(X + Y) \leq CX$ if and only if $CY \leq 0$.

We shall obtain a contradiction to the above by assuming that the maximal extreme vector $\overline{X}$ is not an optimal vector. Then, in fact, by the criterion of optimality just developed, there will exist a vector Y such that $\overline{X} + Y \geq 0$, $AY = 0$, and $CY > 0$. The vector $\overline{X} + Y$ is a feasible vector, but it cannot be an extreme vector of F_P, because $C(\overline{X} + Y) > C\overline{X}$, and $\overline{X}$ was a maximal extreme vector.

The set $Q_{\overline{X}}$ of active indices for $\overline{X}$ will be of special interest along with the set R_Y of indices J such that $Y_J \neq 0$. Since the vectors A_J for $J \in Q_{\overline{X}}$ are independent (because $\overline{X}$ is an extreme point of F_P), while the vectors A_J for $J \in R_Y$ are dependent (because $AY = 0$), we see that R_Y contains at least one value of J not in $Q_{\overline{X}}$; let S_Y denote the set of those values of J in R_Y but not in $Q_{\overline{X}}$. We know that $\bar{x}_J + y_J \geq 0$ because $\overline{X} + Y \geq 0$; if $J \epsilon S_Y$ then $\bar{x}_J = 0$ and $y_J \neq 0$, whence $y_J > 0$.

We observe next that there must be a value of J such that $y_J < 0$. Otherwise, in fact, $y_J > 0$ for every $J \epsilon R_Y$, $\overline{X} + vY$ would be feasible for any $v \geq 0$, and $f(\overline{X} + vY) = C\overline{X} + vCY$ could take on arbitrarily large values, contradicting our knowledge that f is bounded above on F_P. Furthermore, since $\overline{X} + Y \geq 0$, if $y_J < 0$ then $J \epsilon Q_{\overline{X}}$. We now choose $v_0 > 1$ in such a way as to keep $\overline{X} + v_0 Y \geq 0$ and so that $\bar{x}_J + v_0 y_J = 0$ for some $J \epsilon Q_{\overline{X}}$ for which $y_J < 0$; define $Z = v_0 Y = [z_J]^t$. Delete from $Q_{\overline{X}}$ all values of J for which $\bar{x}_J + z_J = 0$ and denote by Q_0 the set of those values of J remaining in $Q_{\overline{X}}$; Q_0 is assuredly a proper subset of $Q_{\overline{X}}$, and we do not care whether or not Q_0 is empty.

We now have the vector $\overline{X} + Z = [\bar{x}_J + z_J]^t$ with

$$\bar{x}_J + z_J > 0 \qquad\qquad (J \epsilon Q_0),$$

$$\bar{x}_J = 0, \qquad z_J > 0 \qquad (J \epsilon S_Y),$$

$$\bar{x}_J = z_J = 0 \qquad\qquad \text{otherwise.}$$

Let T denote the set of all values of J belonging either to Q_0 or to S_Y; actually,

$$T = Q_{\overline{X}+Z}.$$

If the vectors A $(J \epsilon T)$ are independent then $\overline{X} + Z$ is an *extreme* vector—one of the vectors X_h $(h = 1, \cdots, e)$—with the property that

$$CX_h = C\overline{X} + CZ > C\overline{X},$$

contradicting the maximality of $\overline{X}$ among the extreme vectors and completing the proof in this case.

If the vectors A_J $(J \epsilon T)$ are dependent, then we shall complete the proof by showing, roughly speaking, that we can omit enough of them to arrive at an independent set without decreasing the value of f, thus obtaining again an extreme vector at which the value of f exceeds the value at $\overline{X}$ and again contradicting the maximality of $\overline{X}$.

If the vectors A_J $(J \epsilon T)$ are dependent then there exist u_J $(J \epsilon T)$, not all zero, such that

$$\Sigma_J A_J u_J = 0 \qquad (J \epsilon T),$$

and we define $U = [u_J]^t$ with $u_J = 0$ if $J \epsilon' T$. By multiplying U by a nonzero number, if necessary, we assure that

$$0 \leq |u_J| \leq \bar{x}_J + z_J \qquad (J \epsilon T).$$

Then the vectors $V_{\pm} = \overline{X} + Z \pm U$ are both feasible. There are two cases, according as $CU \neq 0$ or $CU = 0$.

(1) If $CU = 0$ then we choose the sign and adjust the size of U so that

$$\bar{x}_J + z_J + u_J = 0$$

for at least one value of $J \epsilon T$.

(2) If $CU \neq 0$, we choose the sign so that $CU > 0$. Then, as in proving that $Q_{\overline{X}}$ had a value of J such that $y_J < 0$, we see that T must have a value of J such that $u_J < 0$; otherwise $\overline{X} + Z + vU$ would be feasible for $v \geq 0$, and $C\overline{X} + CZ + vCU$ could take on arbitrarily large values. We now adjust the length of U so that

$$\overline{x}_J + z_J + u_J = 0$$

for some value of $J \epsilon T$ for which $u_J < 0$.

In either case, the resulting vector $V = \overline{X} + Z + U$ is feasible, has

$$f(V) = C\overline{X} + CZ + CU \geq C\overline{X} + CZ \, (> C\overline{X}),$$

and has at least one less active index than $\overline{X} + Z$ had. The process can be continued until the set of active A_J is independent and the corresponding extreme vector X_h has $f(X_h) > f(\overline{X})$, contradicting the maximality of $\overline{X}$.

We conclude that *each maximal extreme vector of* F_P *is an optimal vector of* F_P. There may be optimal vectors, of course, that are not extreme vectors; if X and Y are distinct optimal vectors—maximal extreme vectors, for example—then if $0 < t < 1$ the vector $(1 - t)X + tY$ is easily seen to be feasible and optimal, although clearly not an extreme vector.

The simplex method starts with an extreme vector X. It is possible to decide rather easily whether or not X is optimal. If X is not optimal the calculations lead to a second extreme point, Y, such that $f(X) \leq f(Y)$. Even if $f(Y) = f(X)$, moreover, continuation of the process cannot lead back to X or to any extreme vector already tried. As long as no optimal point has been found, the process goes on. Since the number of optimal points is finite, however, the process must terminate. The extreme point then available is an optimal point.

7. The Simplex Method; Tableaux

The symbol $Q = (q_\alpha) \, (\alpha = 1, \cdots, m)$ will henceforth denote a set of m distinct indices $q_1, \cdots, q_m$ chosen from $1, \cdots, N$; the symbol R will denote the residual set $J = 1, \cdots, N, \, J \, \epsilon' \, Q$.

A tableau is an array of the form

			c_1	$\cdots$	c_J	$\cdots$	c_N
C_Q	A_Q	B	A_1	$\cdots$	A_J	$\cdots$	A_N
c_{q_1}	A_{q_1}	x_{q_1}	a_{11}	$\cdots$	a_{1J}	$\cdots$	a_{1N}
$\vdots$	$\vdots$	$\vdots$	$\vdots$		$\vdots$		$\vdots$
c_{q_m}	A_{q_m}	x_{q_m}	a_{m1}	$\cdots$	a_{mJ}	$\cdots$	a_{mN}
	z_J	$C_Q \cdot B$	$C_Q \cdot A_1$	$\cdots$	$C_Q \cdot A_J$	$\cdots$	$C_Q \cdot A_N$
z_J	$- \, c_J$		$z_1 - c_1$	$\cdots$	$z_J - c_J$	$\cdots$	$z_N - c_N$

The m vectors A_Q will always be independent and therefore a basis for the space of m-component column vectors; they determine the entire tableau. The m numbers $a_{\alpha J}$ in column J are the components of A_J with respect to A_Q; that is,

$$A_J = \Sigma_\alpha A_{q_\gamma} a_{\alpha J};$$

in particular,

$$a_{\alpha q_\beta} = \delta_{q_\alpha q_\beta} \qquad (\alpha, \beta = 1, \cdots, m),$$

for the q_βth column has one in the βth row (that is, when and only when $q_\alpha = q_\beta$) and zero elsewhere. With $x_J = 0$ for $J \epsilon R$, the X with x_{q_α} in the column under B has

$$B = \Sigma_\alpha A_{q_\alpha} x_{q_\alpha} \qquad \text{and} \qquad x_{q_\alpha} \geq 0.$$

Since the A_Q are independent, X is not only feasible but extreme as well. We see that

$$f(X) = \Sigma_\alpha c_{q_\alpha} x_{q_\alpha} = C_Q \cdot X.$$

The first tableau may be read off directly from the prepared problem as in the accompanying illustration. The set Q is $1, \cdots, m$, $q_\alpha = \alpha$, $x_{q_\alpha} = b_\alpha$, and $c_{q_\alpha} = -M$ for $\alpha = 1, \cdots, g + e$, while $c_{q_\alpha} = 0$ for $\alpha = g + e + 1, \cdots, m$, and

$$f(X) = -M \sum_{\alpha=1}^{g+e} b_\alpha.$$

Here, and in later tableaux, the M's in z_J and $z_J - c_J$ may be carried along separately, perhaps in an accompanying secondary row (as in the example at the end of Section 9, p. 35). Here again, as in later tableaux, it is readily seen that

$$z_{q_\alpha} = c_{q_\alpha} \qquad (\alpha = 1, \cdots, m).$$

A sufficient condition for the optimality of X may be given at once: If

$$z_J - c_J \geq 0 \qquad (J = 1, \cdots, N)$$

in a tableau then the vector X determined by x_{q_α}, with $x_J = 0$ for $J \epsilon R$, is optimal. In fact let Y be feasible. Since $Y \geq 0$,

$$f(Y) = \Sigma_J c_J y_J \leq \Sigma_J z_J y_J = \Sigma_J \Sigma_\alpha c_{q_\alpha} a_{\alpha J} y_J = \Sigma_\alpha c_{q_\alpha} \Sigma_J a_{\alpha J} y_J.$$

At the same time,

$$B = \Sigma_J A_J y_J = \Sigma_J \Sigma_\alpha A_{q_\alpha} a_{\alpha J} y_J = \Sigma_\alpha A_{q_\alpha} \Sigma_J a_{\alpha J} y_J = \Sigma_\alpha A_{q_\alpha} x_{q_\alpha}.$$

Since the vectors A_{q_α} are independent,

$$\Sigma_J a_{\alpha J} y_J = x_{q_\alpha},$$

whence

$$f(Y) \leq \Sigma_\alpha c_{q_\alpha} x_{q_\alpha} = f(X)$$

and X is optimal. As we shall see at the end of Section 8, and shall meanwhile assume, this condition is also necessary.

Example. Although details of the calculation will not be clear until later on, we introduce here a fairly complete illustration (taken with permission from Chapter II of [18]). We shall see in this instance how to pass from the original problem to the prepared problem, how to set up the initial tableau, how to decide when the problem has been finished, and where to locate the solution in the tableau then at hand. Another example is at the end of Section 9.

The problem concerns an allocation of materials to two procedures for making fuel oil from pitch and flux stock, the latter being available in any desired quantity. One method is to blend the pitch directly with flux stock. The other procedure is first to use the pitch to make tar, and then to blend the tar with flux stock to make the fuel oil.

Suppose that P gallons per hour of pitch are mixed directly with flux stock, while V gallons per hour of pitch are used to make tar which is then mixed with flux stock. Each gallon of pitch used to make tar will yield 0.8 gallon of tar and by-products of negligible value. If a total of F gallons per hour of flux stock are used then the output of fuel oil will be $P + 0.8V + F$ gallons per hour.

The fuel oil is worth 5 cents per gallon and the flux stock is worth 8 cents per gallon, and the producer has reasons for neglecting in this particular calculation the cost of pitch, of pitch-to-tar conversion, and of tar. The net value of the output will therefore be

$$5(P + 0.8V + F) - 8F = 5P + 4V - 3F \text{ cents per hour,}$$

and it is this figure that the producer desires to maximize.

The fuel oil must meet certain specifications as to viscosity and specific gravity. These technical requirements turn out (we omit details) to be expressed respectively by the inequalities $2P + V - 2F \leq 0$ and $P + V - 3F \leq 0$. The producer has a source of pitch delivering 1000 gallons per hour, and clearly cannot use pitch at a rate faster than this, whence $P + V \leq 1000$.

From its practical source, the problem accordingly is this:

Maximize
$$5P + 4V - 3F$$
subject to
$$P \geq 0, \qquad V \geq 0, \qquad F \geq 0,$$
$$2P + V - 2F \leq 0,$$
$$P + V - 3F \leq 0,$$
$$P + V \qquad \leq 1000.$$

Here $m = 3$. Since the numbers 0, 0, and 1000 on the right are all ≥ 0, $b_\alpha \geq 0$ ($\alpha = 1, 2, 3$) and there is no need to multiply any inequality by -1. Since $g = e = 0$ (neither "≥ 0" nor "$=$" occurs in the constraints), there is no need to reorder the constraints. The original problem, problem (p) of (5.1), therefore results from a mere renaming of the variables $x_4 = P$, $x_5 = V$, and $x_6 = F$. Thus problem (p) is this:

TABLEAUX

c_j			0	0	0	5	4	−3	
C_Q	A_Q	B	A_1	A_2	A_3	A_4	A_5	A_6	
0	A_1	0	1	0	0	2	1	−2	min $(z_J − c_J) = −5$, so A_4 in
0	out A_2	0	0	1	0	1	1	−3	min "B/A_4^{+}" = 0 twice (degener-
0	A_3	1000	0	0	1	1	1	0	acy); tie broken in first col; A_2 out
	z_J	0	0	0	0	0 (in)	0	0	
$z_J − c_J$			0	0	0	− 5	− 4	3	
0	out A_1	0	1	− 2	0	0	− 1	4	min $(z_J − c_J) = −12$, so A_6 in
5	A_4	0	0	1	0	1	1	− 3	
0	A_3	1000	0	− 1	1	0	0	3	min "B/A_6^{+}" = 0, so A_1 out
	z_J	0	0	5	0	5	5 (in)	− 15	
$z_J − c_J$			0	5	0	0	1	− 12	
− 3	A_6	0	$\frac{1}{4}$	− $\frac{1}{2}$	0	0	− $\frac{1}{4}$	1	min $(z_J − c_J) = −2$, so A_5 in
5	out A_4	0	$\frac{3}{4}$	− $\frac{1}{2}$	0	1	$\frac{1}{4}$	0	
0	A_3	1000	− $\frac{3}{4}$	$\frac{1}{2}$	1	0	$\frac{3}{4}$	0	min "B/A_5^{+}" = 0, so A_4 out
	z_J	0	3	− 1	0	5 (in)	2	− 3	
$z_J − c_J$			3	− 1	0	0	− 2	0	
− 3	A_6	0	1	− 1	0	1	0	1	min $(z_J − c_J) = −5$, so A_2 in
4	A_5	0	3	− 2	0	4	1	0	
0	out A_3	1000	− 3	2	1	− 3	0	0	min "B/A_2^{+}" = 500, so A_3 out
	z_J	0	9 (in)	− 5	0	13	4	− 3	
$z_J − c_J$			9	− 5	0	8	0	0	
− 3	A_6	500	− $\frac{1}{2}$	0	$\frac{1}{2}$	− $\frac{1}{2}$	0	1	min $(z_J − c_J) = 0$; finished
4	A_5	1000	0	0	1	1	1	0	
0	A_2	500	− $\frac{3}{2}$	1	$\frac{1}{2}$	− $\frac{3}{2}$	0	0	
	z_J	2500	$\frac{3}{2}$	0	$\frac{5}{2}$	$\frac{11}{2}$	4	− 3	under conditions, max $5P + 4V − 3F$ is 2500, attained
$z_J − c_J$			$\frac{3}{2}$	0	$\frac{5}{2}$	$\frac{1}{2}$	0	0	for $P = 0$, $V = 1000$, $F = 500$

Maximize
$$f(x) = 5x_4 + 4x_5 - 3x_6$$

subject to
$$x_j \geq 0 \qquad (j = 4, 5, 6),$$
$$2x_4 + x_5 - 2x_6 \leq 0,$$

Problem (p)

$$x_4 + x_5 - 3x_6 \leq 0,$$
$$x_4 + x_5 \qquad\quad \leq 1000.$$

To pass to the prepared problem we observe that each constraint involves "$\leq$" and therefore introduce slack variables x_1, x_2, and x_3, coefficients $c_1 = c_2 = c_3 = 0$, and constraints $x_1 \geq 0$, $x_2 \geq 0$, and $x_3 \geq 0$, arriving in this way at problem (P):

Maximize
$$5x_4 + 4x_5 - 3x_6$$

subject to
$$x_J \geq 0 \qquad (J = 1, \cdots, 6)$$

Problem (P)

$$x_1 \quad\;\; + 2x_4 + x_5 - 2x_6 = 0,$$
$$x_2 + x_4 + x_5 - 3x_6 = 0,$$
$$x_3 + x_4 + x_5 \qquad\quad = 1000.$$

The first (topmost) of the accompanying tableaux is developed directly from problem (P) in the way described above. Since $C_Q = 0$, $f(X) = 0$. Since X has $x_J = 0$ except that $x_3 = 1000$, X is extreme. On the other hand, $z_J - c_J < 0$ for $J = 4$ and $J = 5$, whence X is not optimal.

Neglecting temporarily the passage from one tableau to another, let us inspect the last (bottom) tableau. Since $z_J - c_J \geq 0$ ($J = 1, \cdots, 6$), we have located an optimal X—namely,
$$X = (0, 500, 0, 0, 1000, 500).$$

The maximum value of $f(X)$ under the constraints of the problem is
$$C_Q \cdot B = 0 \cdot 500 + 4 \cdot 1000 + (-3) \cdot 500 = 2500.$$

In the practical problem, the conclusion is that, subject to the constraints, the maximum net value of the output of fuel oil is \$25 per hour, obtained (since $P = 0$ and $V = 1000$) by first changing all the pitch to tar and then (since $F = 500$) adding 500 gallons of flux stock.

We are now ready to discuss in detail the procedure for generating the succession of tableaux leading to the solution of the prepared problem.

Suppose that a tableau has $z_J - c_J < 0$ for some value of J. We conclude that X in that tableau is not an optimal vector and therefore examine the possibility of increasing $f(X) = C_Q \cdot X$ by changing the basis appearing in the column A_Q. The process will consist in choosing an index k in R and an index

r in Q, transferring k to Q and r to R, replacing A_r in A_Q by A_k, and calculating the entries in the tableau determined by the new A_Q.

It will turn out after k and r have been chosen that $a_{rk} > 0$. Let us show at once that if $r = q_\rho \in Q$, $k \in R$, and $a_{rk} \neq 0$ then the vectors A_k and A_{q_α} ($\alpha \neq \rho$) are independent. Otherwise there would exist constants d and d_α ($\alpha \neq \rho$), not all zero, such that

$$dA_k + \sum_{\alpha \neq \rho} d_\alpha A_{q_\alpha} = 0.$$

If d were zero we could conclude that the vectors A_{q_α} ($\alpha \neq \rho$) were dependent, contradicting the fact that the A_{q_α} form a basis; hence $d \neq 0$. It follows that A_k is a linear combination of the A_{q_α} for $q_\alpha \neq r$. But $A_k = \sum_\alpha A_{q_\alpha} a_{\alpha k}$, the coefficients $a_{\alpha k}$ are unique, and $a_{rk} \neq 0$. From this contradiction we conclude that the vectors A_k and A_{q_α} ($q_\alpha \neq r$) are indeed independent. It follows that the new vector X will be another extreme vector of F_P.

Let k be an index in R and study the effect of introducing A_k into the basis with a coefficient θ. From the identity

$$B = \sum_\alpha A_{q_\alpha} x_{q_\alpha} - \theta A_k + \theta A_k = \sum_\alpha A_{q_\alpha}(x_{q_\alpha} - \theta a_{\alpha k}) + \theta A_k \qquad (7.1)$$

and the feasibility requirements, we conclude that we must choose θ so that $\theta \geq 0$ and $x_{q_\alpha} - \theta a_{\alpha k} \geq 0$ ($\alpha = 1, \cdots, m$). At the same time, we wish actually to remove at least one vector, and will therefore seek to have $x_{q_\alpha} - \theta a_{\alpha k} = 0$ for at least one value of α.

The new value of f will be   (7.2)

$$\sum_\alpha c_{q_\alpha}(x_{q_\alpha} - \theta a_{\alpha k}) + c_k \theta = C_Q \cdot X - \theta(C_Q \cdot A_k - c_k) = C_Q \cdot X - \theta(z_k - c_k).$$

Some increase in f may be possible if, as we are assuming, there is a value of J for which $z_J - c_J < 0$. We choose a k for which $z_k - c_k$ is least; among several k with least $z_k - c_k$ we choose the least value of k. The vector A_k is to be brought into the basis.

With k fixed, we inspect the column of numbers $a_{\alpha k}$. If $a_{\alpha k} \leq 0$ ($\alpha = 1, \cdots, m$) then we see from (7.1) and the feasibility requirements that, if the vector Y has components $y_{q_\alpha} = x_{q_\alpha} - \theta a_{\alpha k}$ ($\alpha = 1, \cdots, m$), $y_k = \theta$, and $y_J = 0$ otherwise, then Y will be feasible for arbitrarily large values of θ. It is then also evident, since $z_k - c_k < 0$ in the last expression in (7.2), that $f(Y)$ can be made arbitrarily large. Since this contradicts our knowledge that f is bounded on F_P, we conclude that $a_{\alpha k} > 0$ for at least one value of α. Letting β run over those values of α for which $a_{\alpha k} > 0$, we define

$$\theta = \min_\beta \frac{x_{q_\beta}}{a_{\beta k}}. \qquad (7.3)$$

So defined, $\theta = 0$ if and only if $x_{q_\beta} = 0$ for some value of β with $a_{\beta k} > 0$. In the first tableau of the illustration $k = 4$, $\beta = 1, 2, 3$, and $\theta = 0$ because $x_1 = x_2 = 0$. If $\theta = 0$ the value of f will be unchanged, but we introduce A_k

into the basis nevertheless; the effect, as we shall see, is to pass to another extreme point, a further step from which may increase f. (The mnemonic symbol B/A_k^+ may be helpful.)

Having chosen k and θ, we must choose a vector A_r to remove from the basis. If the minimum in (7.3) occurs for just one value of β—say ρ—and $q_\rho = r$, then we remove A_r.

If the minimum in (7.3) occurs for several values of β, a "degeneracy" is said to have arisen. The coefficients $x_{q_\alpha} - \theta a_{\alpha k}$ of several A_Q will become zero in (7.1); these vectors will not be active in the next tableau. Geometrically, this means simply that B is in the subspace, of dimension less than m, spanned by A_k (if $\theta > 0$) and those A_Q with $x_{q_\alpha} > \theta a_{\alpha k}$. In fact, B is always in the subspace spanned by the active vectors of the basis in any tableau; in the illustration, B is in the one-dimensional subspace spanned by the vector A_3 in the basis in the first tableau. Staying in a subspace of dimension less than m, however, might exclude extreme vectors and thus invite failure to locate optimal vectors. Some inactive vectors of a basis may become active vectors in a later basis. In the illustration, for example, A_2 has the coefficient zero in the first tableau (indeed, it is removed forthwith from the basis); in the final tableau, however, A_2 has not only reentered the basis, but has also become an active vector, with coefficient 500. A method is needed to "break the tie," selecting just one vector A_r for removal from the basis.

We give Charnes' rule of selection (see [2] 63ff. and [7] Chap. 7), which makes degeneracy demonstrably harmless. Examples are known (cf. [7] 107) in which certain less sophisticated methods of selection lead to cycling.

The aim is to choose one vector A_{q_ρ} among the several for which the minimum in (7.3) occurs. Let the index γ_1 run over those values only of β for which this happens. A_{q_ρ} must be chosen from among the $A_{q_{\gamma_1}}$, which we may call competing vectors. Charnes' method carries the competition, which is indecisive in column B, successively into columns 1, 2, 3, $\cdots$ of the tableau. Vectors fall out of competition until a stage is reached at which there is only one survivor. If that vector is A_{q_ρ}, and $q_\rho = r$, then A_r is removed from the basis.

The first step in Charnes' method is to divide each row γ_1 still in the competition by the positive number $a_{\gamma_1 k}$. One then enters the first column, seeking

$$\theta_1 = \min_{\gamma_1} \frac{a_{\gamma_1 1}}{a_{\gamma_1 k}}.$$

If this minimum (which may be negative) occurs for only one value of γ_1—say, $\gamma_1 = \rho$—then A_{q_ρ} is to be removed from the basis. Otherwise, let γ_2 range over those values only of γ_1 for which θ_1 is attained, enter the second column, and seek

$$\theta_2 = \min_{\gamma_2} \frac{a_{\gamma_2 2}}{a_{\gamma_2 k}}.$$

If this minimum occurs only once—say, for $\gamma_2 = \rho$— then A_{q_ρ} is to be removed from the basis. Continuing inductively, if

$$\theta_h = \min_{\gamma_h} \frac{a_{\gamma_h h}}{a_{\gamma_h k}}$$

is attained for several values of γ_h, let γ_{h+1} range over those values only of γ_h for which θ_h is attained and seek

$$\theta_{h+1} = \min_{\gamma_{h+1}} \frac{a_{\gamma_{h+1} h+1}}{a_{\gamma_{h+1} k}};$$

selection is decisive, or not, according as θ_{h+1} is attained for just one value of γ_{h+1}, or for several.

It must be shown, of course, that this rule of selection is effective in the sense that a stage will necessarily be reached in which there is just one surviving vector A_{q_ρ}. The proof rests on the fact that each tableau contains m columns—namely, A_{q_α}—that are a rearrangement of the columns of the $m \times m$ identity matrix. Any subset of m' rows ($1 \le m' \le m$) in the body of a tableau will intersect the columns A_{q_α} in columns (with m' entries) that are a rearrangement of the columns of an $m' \times m'$ identity matrix. In the rows γ_1 competing in the first column, the elements in the columns $A_{q_{\gamma_1}}$, on division by the $a_{\gamma_1 k}$, remain zero except for $a_{\gamma_1 q_{\gamma_1}}$, which changes from unity to $1/a_{\gamma_1 k}$.

Now suppose that, at some stage, $A_{q_{\alpha_0}}$ is still in the competition, and column q_{α_0} is the (next) one in which a minimum ratio is to be sought. The ratio is $1/a_{q_{\alpha_0}} > 0$ in row q_{α_0}, and zero elsewhere. Hence $A_{q_{\alpha_0}}$ is eliminated from the competition when (at the latest) column q_{α_0} is reached. If rows γ_h are still in the competition, therefore, columns q_{γ_h} are still to the right. The competition continues, column by column, from left to right, until the algebraic minimum, which always is attained at least once, occurs at most once. If A_{q_ρ} is the (sole) surviving vector, and $q_\rho = r$, then A_r is to be removed from the basis; an unambiguous decision has been reached.

The numbers θ_h play no further part in the calculation, unless they turn up again, quite accidentally, in the effort to settle ties in later tableaux. The rows γ_1, moreover, should now be multiplied by $a_{\gamma_1 k}$ in order to restore the tableau to its preselection state.

We shall use Charnes' rule and his perturbation technique later to establish the effectiveness of the simplex method. Let us observe at the moment that our illustrative example has a degeneracy in the first tableau. In it, $k = 4$, and

$$\frac{x_1}{a_{14}} = \frac{0}{2} = 0 = \frac{0}{1} = \frac{x_2}{a_{24}},$$

so $\gamma_1 = 1, 2$. Division by $a_{\gamma_1 k}$ halves the first row and reproduces the second. The tie is broken in the first column, for

$$\frac{a_{11}}{a_{14}} = \frac{1}{2} > 0 = \frac{a_{21}}{a_{24}}.$$

Hence $r = 2$, and A_2 is to be removed from the basis.

Having shown earlier that A_k and A_{q_α} $(\alpha \neq r)$ are independent, we are ready to pass from the old tableau to the new. The index r is transferred from Q to R, while k is transferred from R to Q; the new value of q_ρ is k. In the column A_Q, accordingly, A_{q_ρ} is now A_k. In the column C_Q, c_r is replaced by c_k. While the order of rows and columns in the body $[a_{\alpha J}]$ of the tableau is always preserved, the order of the elements in the columns C_Q, A_Q, and B is taken as it comes from the above rules.

The number $a_{\rho k}$, often called the "pivotal element," is positive. Divide the entire ρth row, including x_{q_ρ}, by $a_{\rho k}$, obtaining a unit in the ρ, k position. Use this unit and row operations on the matrix $[b_{q_\alpha} a_{\alpha J}]$ to reduce to zero every other element in the kth column. Similarly, multiply the ρth row by the old value of $z_k - c_k$ and subtract from the row at the very bottom of the tableau, getting $z_k - c_k = 0$ in the new tableau. The row z_J in the new tableau may be obtained either by adding c_J to $z_J - c_J$ in the new row below or by calculating $C_Q \cdot A_J$ directly *(check?)*. Many books give easily developed formulas for these operations.

In any tableau, the matrix $[a_{\alpha\beta}]$ in the first m columns of $[a_{\alpha J}]$ has arisen by performing on the $m \times m$ identity matrix in the first m columns of the first tableau the same row operations as on all columns A_J of the first tableau, which we write, for the moment, with a superscript 0: $[\mathring{a}_{\alpha J}]$. For $J \epsilon Q$, A_J is one of the vectors A_{q_α} in the basis, so that

$$a_{\alpha q_\gamma} = \delta_{q_\alpha q_\gamma} = \Sigma_\beta \, a_{\alpha\beta} \mathring{a}_{\beta q_\gamma},$$

whence $[a_{\alpha\beta}]$ is the inverse of the matrix $\mathring{a}_{\beta q_\gamma}$ occurring in the first tableau in those columns A_{q_γ} now in the basis A_Q, taken in order of their occurrence in A_Q. More generally,

$$a_{\alpha J} = \Sigma_\beta \, a_{\alpha\beta} \mathring{a}_{\beta J} \qquad (J = 1, \, \cdots, \, N)$$

$$x_{q_\alpha} = \Sigma_\beta \, a_{\alpha\beta} b_\beta \qquad (\alpha = 1, \, \cdots, \, m). \tag{7.4}$$

It follows that
$$b_\alpha = \Sigma_\beta \, \mathring{a}_{\alpha q_\beta} x_{q_\beta} \tag{7.5}$$

and
$$z_J = \Sigma_\alpha \, c_{q_\alpha} a_{\alpha J} = \Sigma_\alpha \, c_{q_\alpha} \Sigma_\beta \, a_{\alpha\beta} \mathring{a}_{\beta J} = \Sigma_\beta \, z_\beta \mathring{a}_{\beta J}. \tag{7.6}$$

If, in the new tableau, $z_J - c_J < 0$ for some value of J, then X is not optimal and the process is repeated. It is worth noting that the vector A_r that left the basis has new $z_r - c_r$ equal to $- (z_r - c_r)/a_{\rho k} > 0$ (old z_r here), and that A_r is therefore not a candidate for immediate re-entry into the basis. That A_r can come back in is clear from our example, where A_2 is removed at the first step but is in the final basis. We shall see, nevertheless, that the same entire basis cannot recur; hence the process must terminate.

The final tableau has $z_J - c_J \geq 0$ $(J = 1, \, \cdots, \, N)$, indicating that X is optimal. If any of the artificial vectors A_α $(\alpha = 1, \, \cdots, \, g + e)$ are in the final basis, the conclusion, as we have seen, is that the constraints of the original problem are inconsistent; assume this false—in other words, that X is special. Now for $a = 1$, $\cdots$, g, $A_{m+n+\alpha} = -A_\alpha$, so no vector $A_{m+n+\alpha}$ can be in the final basis. For $\alpha = 1$, $\cdots$, g, $c_{m+n+\alpha} = 0$ and $z_{m+n+\alpha} \geq 0$, whence $z_\alpha = -z_{m+n+\alpha} \leq 0$; but $z_\alpha - c_\alpha = z_\alpha + M \geq 0$.

8.   Effectiveness of the Simplex Method

We wish now to show that the simplex method, with Charnes' rule for selection in case of degeneracy, will ultimately produce an optimal vector. The proof ([2] 62-67, [5] 220, and [7] Chap. 7) uses a perturbed problem in which the successive tableaux are the "same" perturbations of the successive unperturbed tableaux. The same vector is chosen at each stage for entrance into the basis. The perturbed problem is never degenerate, the value of the perturbed parameter φ (corresponding to the unperturbed θ of (7.3)) is attained for a unique index, and the vector chosen to be removed from the basis is precisely the one chosen in the unperturbed tableau (if degenerate, by Charnes' selection principle). The value of φ is positive, so that the value of the perturbed objective function always *increases*. Since the basis in the perturbed and unperturbed tableaux contains the same vectors A_Q, and the components x_{q_α} of the unperturbed B with respect to this basis are unique, and of order zero in the perturbation parameter, it follows that the same total basis A_Q cannot recur. The number of possible bases is finite. In spite of degeneracy, therefore, cycling can not occur and an optimal vector is ultimately attained.

The perturbation does not enter into any calculations. It is simply a technical device to make it possible to demonstrate in full generality that the actual calculations will be successful if Charnes' rule of selection is used.

The prepared problem is this:

Maximize

$$f(X) = \Sigma_J c_J x_J$$

with $x_J \geq 0$ and $\Sigma\, a_{\alpha J} x_J = b_\alpha.$

The perturbed problem is this:

Maximize

$$f(P,\epsilon) = \Sigma_J c_J p_J$$

subject to

$$p_J \geq 0 \qquad (J = 1,\, \cdots,\, N)$$

and $\Sigma_J\, a_{\alpha J} p_J = b_\alpha + \Sigma\, a_{\alpha J} \epsilon^J \qquad (\alpha = 1,\, \cdots,\, m),$

where ϵ^J is the Jth power of the *positive* number ϵ.

With each unperturbed tableau there is therefore associated a perturbed tableau. One may imagine a row ϵ^J $(J = 1,\, \cdots,\, n)$ written above the topmost row (c_J) of the tableau. We shall actually write out the perturbation only for column B, writing p_{q_α} there, with x_{q_α} referring to the unperturbed tableau.

The rows z_J and $z_J - c_J$ will be unchanged for $J = 1, \cdots, N$, but in the perturbed tableau

$$C_Q \cdot P = f(P, \epsilon).$$

We shall use ϵ to investigate the effect of passing from one perturbed tableau to the next. The size of ϵ is at our disposal, and it may be decreased in order to bring about desired circumstances. It will always be understood, for one thing, that each polynomial in ϵ has the sign of its constant term, if that term is not zero.

It is evident from the statement of the perturbed problem that, in its first tableau,

$$p_{q_\alpha} = x_{q_\alpha} + \sum_{J=1}^{N} a_{\alpha J} \epsilon^J. \tag{8.1}$$

What is more, in fact, in the first tableau,

$$p_{q_\alpha} = b_{q_\alpha} + \epsilon^\alpha + \sum_{J=m+1}^{N} a_{\alpha J} \epsilon^J. \tag{8.2}$$

Since $b_\alpha \geq 0$, and terms of lower order in ϵ dominate those of higher order, we may choose ϵ so small that in the first tableau,

$$p_{q_\alpha} > 0 \qquad (\alpha = 1, \cdots, m). \tag{8.3}$$

In the first tableau, finally,

$$f(P, \epsilon) = f(X) + \sum_{J=1}^{N} z_J \epsilon^J. \tag{8.4}$$

We shall show by induction that each perturbed tableau has properties (8.1), (8.3), and (8.4).

Equations (8.1) merely say, of course, that successive tableaux of the perturbed problem are the "same" perturbations of successive tableaux of the unperturbed problem. Property (8.3) says that in the perturbed problem each vector of the basis A_Q is active. Since (8.4) is a consequence of (8.1), it will suffice to prove (8.1) and (8.3).

Now the choice of a vector A_k to be brought into the basis uses the row $z_J - c_J$, and will therefore be the same in the perturbed as in the unperturbed tableaux.

With k fixed, the next step is to use those values β of α for which $a_{\alpha k} > 0$ and to seek (using 8.1)

$$\varphi = \min_\beta \frac{p_{q_\beta}}{a_{\beta k}} = \min_\beta \frac{x_{q_\beta} + \sum\limits_{J=1}^{N} a_{\beta J} \epsilon^J}{a_{\beta k}}. \tag{8.5}$$

By (8.3), $\varphi > 0$.

If the situation in the unperturbed tableau is nondegenerate then the respective minima occur for the same unique value β_0 of β. If $x_{\beta_0} > 0$ this is obvious.

If $x_{\beta_0} = 0$ then β_0 is the only value of α in which the numerator on the right has only positive powers of ϵ.

If there is a degeneracy in the unperturbed tableau, then in the perturbed tableau one will be comparing competing polynomials

$$g_\beta(\epsilon) = \frac{x_{q_\beta}}{a_{\beta k}} + \sum_{J=1}^{N} \frac{a_{\beta J}}{a_{\beta k}} \epsilon^J$$

having the same constant term. A comparison of coefficients of the terms in ϵ^J corresponds to competition in column J according to Charnes' selection principle for the unperturbed tableau. Polynomials in which ϵ does not have a minimal coefficient are discarded, coefficients of terms in ϵ^2 are compared in surviving polynomials, and so on, until, as in the unperturbed tableau, a unique minimal coefficient is reached—say, $a_{\rho J_0}/a_{\rho k}$.

Now it is conceivable that unwelcome behavior of higher-order terms might keep $g_\rho(\epsilon)$ from being a minimum among those still competing with coefficients of ϵ^{J_0}, but this may be avoided by decreasing ϵ. In this way we arrive at the minimum φ of (8.5) for a *unique* value ρ of β. Degeneracy can always be avoided in the perturbed tableau.

We also arrive, therefore, at the same index r for the vector A_r to be removed from the basis. Since φ occurs only for $\beta = \rho$, it follows further in the new perturbed tableau that $p'_{q_\alpha} = p_{q_\alpha} - \varphi a_{\alpha k} > 0$ if $\alpha \neq \rho$. Since φ itself enters the column under B as p'_{q_ρ}, and $\varphi > 0$, we see that the new tableau has property (8.3). Since the pivotal element $a_{\rho k}$ is the same, the row operations will be the same on the perturbed tableau. It follows that equations (8.1) will hold in the new perturbed tableau.

Using primes to distinguish quantities from the new tableau, we now note that

$$f(P',\epsilon) = \Sigma_\alpha c_{q_\alpha} p'_{q_\alpha} = \Sigma_\alpha c_{q_\alpha}(p_{q_\alpha} - \varphi a_{\alpha k}) + c_k \varphi = f(P,\epsilon) - \varphi(z_k - c_k).$$

Since $z_k - c_k < 0$ and $\varphi > 0$, it is clear that $f(P',\epsilon) > f(P,\epsilon)$ and the objective function does increase. Since components with respect to a basis such as A_Q are unique, a basis once used cannot recur and the process necessarily terminates.

Unless a tableau has $z_J - c_J \geq 0$ $(J = 1, \cdots, N)$ the process requires a step to a further tableau; this condition is therefore necessary as well as sufficient in order that the vector X in a tableau be optimal. For a geometric discussion see [7] 66-68.

9. Solution of the Dual Problem

Suppose that an optimal X has been found for the primal problem. The existence theorem of Section 3 tells us that then the dual problem has feasible vectors and, indeed, an optimal one U, which will have $UB = CX$. Our aim in this final section is to demonstrate that *the vector* $U = (u_\alpha) = (z_\alpha)$ *whose components are the* m *numbers* z_α $(\alpha = 1, \cdots, $ m$)$ *in the row* z_J *(last row but one)* *in the final tableau is an optimal vector for the dual of the original problem.*

We first obtain the dual, as in Section 2, of the original problem (p). To this end all the constraints (h_α) must be expressed as inequalities of the form "$\leq$." For $\alpha = 1, \cdots, g$, multiply by -1, getting

$$- \Sigma_j\, a_{\alpha j} x_j \leq - b_\alpha.$$

For $\alpha = g + 1, \cdots, g + e$, replace each equation by two inequalities,

$$\Sigma_j\, a_{\alpha j} x_j \leq b_\alpha$$

and

$$- \Sigma_j\, a_{\alpha j} x_j \leq - b_\alpha.$$

For $\alpha = g + e + 1, \cdots, m$, no change is needed. The primal problem now requires a maximum of $\Sigma c_j x_j$ subject to the constraints $x_j \geq 0$ and

$$\Sigma_j\, (- a_{\alpha j}) x_j \leq - b_\alpha \qquad (\alpha = 1, \cdots, g)$$

$$\Sigma_j\, a_{\alpha j} x_j \leq b_\alpha \qquad \Sigma_j\, (- a_{\alpha j}) x_j \leq - b_\alpha \qquad (\alpha = g + 1, \cdots, g + e)$$

$$\Sigma_j\, a_{\alpha j} \leq b_\alpha \qquad (\alpha = g + e + 1, \cdots, m)$$

The dual of this problem, as defined in Section 1, is to minimize

$$\sum_{\alpha=1}^{g} t_\alpha(- b_\alpha) + \sum_{\alpha=g+1}^{g+e} [v_\alpha b_\alpha + w_\alpha(- b_\alpha)] + \sum_{\alpha=g+e+1}^{m} u_\alpha b_\alpha$$

subject to the constraints $t_\alpha \geq 0$, $v_\alpha \geq 0$, $w_\alpha \geq 0$, $u_\alpha \geq 0$, and, for $j = m + 1$, $\cdots, m + n$,

$$\sum_{\alpha=1}^{g} t_\alpha(- a_{\alpha j}) + \sum_{\alpha=g+1}^{g+e} [v_\alpha a_{\alpha j} + w_\alpha(- a_{\alpha j})] + \sum_{\alpha=g+e+1}^{m} u_\alpha a_{\alpha j} \geq c_j.$$

Simplifications are possible. For $\alpha = 1, \cdots, g$, put $u_\alpha = - t_\alpha$, with $u_\alpha \leq 0$. For $\alpha = g + 1, \cdots, g + e$, observe that $v_\alpha - w_\alpha$ with $v_\alpha \geq 0$ and $w_\alpha \geq 0$ may be any real number and write $v_\alpha - w_\alpha = u_\alpha$ with no restriction on the sign of u_α. The dual problem now is to minimize

$$\sum_{\alpha=1}^{m} u_\alpha b_\alpha$$

subject to the constraints

$$\Sigma_\alpha\, u_\alpha a_{\alpha j} \geq c_j \qquad (j = m + 1, \cdots, m + n) \qquad (9.1)$$

and

$$u_\alpha \leq 0 \qquad (\alpha = 1, \cdots, g)$$

$$u_\alpha \text{ unrestricted} \qquad (\alpha = g + 1, \cdots, g + e)$$

$$u_\alpha \geq 0 \qquad (\alpha = g + e + 1, \cdots, m).$$

Now we examine the numbers z_α $(\alpha = 1, \cdots, m)$ in the final tableau of the primal problem. We have observed, to begin with, at the end of Section 7 that, for $\alpha = 1, \cdots, g$,

$$z_{m+n+\alpha} - c_{m+n+\alpha} = z_{m+n+\alpha} \geq 0,$$

whence

$$z_\alpha = - z_{m+n+\alpha} \leq 0 \qquad (\alpha = 1, \cdots, g).$$

(The vectors $A_{m+n+\alpha}$, which have now served their theoretical purpose, have in any tableau the property that $A_{m+n+\alpha} = - A_\alpha$ $(\alpha = 1, \cdots, g)$. They are therefore quite superfluous to any actual calculation and need not even be written down.)

For $\alpha = g + e + 1, \cdots, m$, moreover,

$$z_\alpha = z_\alpha - c_\alpha \geq 0.$$

The numbers $u_\alpha = z_\alpha$ ($\alpha = 1, \cdots, m$) therefore satisfy the requirements imposed on their signs.

Next observe that in the final tableau, for $J = 1, \cdots, N$, by (7.6),

$$z_J = \Sigma_\alpha \, c_{q_\alpha} a_{\alpha J} = \Sigma_\alpha \, c_{q_\alpha} \Sigma_\beta \, a_{\alpha\beta} \overset{\circ}{a}_{\beta J} = \Sigma_\beta \, z_\beta \overset{\circ}{a}_{\beta J} \geq c_J$$

where the numbers $\overset{\circ}{a}_{\beta J}$ constitute the body of the initial tableau, and are therefore the same, for $J = m + 1, \cdots, m + n$, as the $a_{\beta j}$ of (9.1). Therefore $u_\alpha = z_\alpha$ ($\alpha = 1, \cdots, m$) satisfy (9.1). Hence $U = (u_\alpha)$ is feasible.

Finally, by (7.6) and (7.4),

$$UB = \Sigma_\alpha \, u_\alpha b_\alpha = \Sigma_\alpha \, z_\alpha b_\alpha = \Sigma_\alpha \, \Sigma_\beta \, c_{q_\beta} a_{\beta\alpha} b_\alpha = \Sigma_\beta \, c_{q_\beta} x_{q_\beta} = CX,$$

where X is optimal. Hence U is optimal.

In the numerical example of Section 7 the dual problem is to minimize $1000u_3$ subject to $u_1 \geq 0$, $u_2 \geq 0$, $u_3 \geq 0$, and

$$
\begin{aligned}
2u_1 + \ u_2 + \ u_3 &\geq 5, \\
u_1 + \ u_2 + \ u_3 &\geq 4, \\
- 2u_2 - 3u_3 &\geq -3.
\end{aligned}
$$

From the final tableau, with $u_\alpha = z_\alpha$ ($\alpha = 1, 2, 3$), an optimal U has $u_1 = \frac{3}{2}$, $u_2 = 0$, and $u_3 = \frac{5}{2}$. As expected, $UB = 2500 = CX$.

Our final example has both slack and artificial vectors.

Example

Original problem

Maximize

$$- x + 3y - 2z$$

subject to

$$
\begin{aligned}
x \geq 0, \quad y \geq 0, \quad z \geq 0 \\
x - 2y + \ z \geq 3, \\
2x + \ y - \ z = 7, \\
x + \ y + 2z \leq 8.
\end{aligned}
$$

Prepared problem

Maximize

$$- Mx_1 - Mx_2 - x_4 + 3x_5 - 2x_6$$

subject to

$$
\begin{aligned}
x_J \geq 0 \quad (J = 1, \cdots, 7) \\
x_1 \ + \ x_4 - 2x_5 + \ x_6 - x_7 &= 3, \\
x_2 + 2x_4 + \ x_5 - \ x_6 &= 7, \\
x_3 + \ x_4 + \ x_5 + 2x_6 &= 8.
\end{aligned}
$$

The variables x_1 and x_2 are artificial, while x_3 and x_7 are slack variables.

TABLEAUX

c_J			$-M$	$-M$	0	-1	3	-2	0
C_Q	A_Q	B	A_1	A_2	A_3	A_4	A_5	A_6	A_7
$-M$ out A_1		3	1	0	0	1	-2	1	-1
$-M$	A_2	7	0	1	0	2	1	-1	0
0	A_3	8	0	0	1	1	1	2	0
z_J		$-10M$	$-M$	$-M$	0	$-3M$ in	M	0	M
$z_J - c_J$			0	0	0	1	-3	2	0
							$-3M$	M		M
-1	A_4	3	1	0	0	1	-2	1	-1
$-M$ out A_2		1	-2	1	0	0	5	-3	2
0	A_3	5	-1	0	1	0	3	1	1
z_J		-3	-1	0	0	-1	2	-1	1
		$-M$	$2M$	$-M$			$-5M$ in	$3M$	$-2M$
$z_J - c_J$			-1	0	0	0	-1	1	1
			$3M$				$-5M$	$3M$	$-2M$
-1	A_4	$\frac{17}{5}$	$\frac{1}{5}$	$\frac{2}{5}$	0	1	0	$-\frac{1}{5}$	$-\frac{1}{5}$
3	A_5	$\frac{1}{5}$	$-\frac{2}{5}$	$\frac{1}{5}$	0	0	1	$-\frac{3}{5}$	$\frac{2}{5}$
0	A_3	$\frac{22}{5}$	$\frac{1}{5}$	$-\frac{3}{5}$	1	0	0	$\frac{14}{5}$	$-\frac{1}{5}$
z_J		$-\frac{14}{5}$	$-\frac{7}{5}$	$\frac{1}{5}$	0	-1	3	$-\frac{8}{5}$	$\frac{7}{5}$
$z_J - c_J$			$-\frac{7}{5}$	$\frac{1}{5}$	0	0	0	$\frac{2}{5}$	$\frac{7}{5}$
			M	M					

Subject to the constraints, max $-Mx_1 - Mx_2 - x_4 + 3x_5 - 2x_6$ is $-\frac{14}{5}$ and is attained for $x_3 = \frac{22}{5}$, $x_4 = \frac{17}{5}$, $x_5 = \frac{1}{5}$, all other $x_J = 0$.

Dual problem

Minimize

$$3u + 7v + 8w$$

subject to

$$u \leq 0, \qquad v \text{ unrestricted}, \qquad w \geq 0$$

$$u + 2v + w \geq -1,$$
$$-2u + v + w \geq 3,$$
$$u - v + 2w \geq -2.$$

From the final tableau, $u = z_1 = -\frac{7}{5}$, $v = z_2 = \frac{1}{5}$, $w = z_3 = 0$. This set of values is feasible, and the minimum subject to the constraints is $-\frac{14}{5}$.

Bibliography

1. Bowman, E. H., and R. B. Fetter, *Analyses of Industrial Operations*, Homewood, Ill.: Irwin, 1959. (Applications)
2. Charnes, A., W. W. Cooper, and A. Henderson, *An Introduction to Linear Programming*, New York: Wiley, 1953.
3. Churchman, C. W., R. L. Ackoff, and E. L. Arnoff, "Linear Programming," chapter in *Introduction to Operations Research*, New York: Wiley, 1957.
4. Dorfman, R., P. A. Samuelson, and R. M. Solow, *Linear Programming and Economic Analysis*, New York: McGraw-Hill, 1957.
5. Eisemann, Kurt, "Linear Programming." *Quart Appl. Math.* 13 (1955) 209-232.
6. Ferguson, Robert O., and Lauren F. Sargent, *Linear Programming*, New York: McGraw-Hill, 1958. (Applications)
7. Gass, Saul I., *Linear Programming*, New York: McGraw-Hill, 1958.
8. Harrison, J. O., Jr., "Linear Programming and Operations Research," chapter in *Operations Research for Management*, J. F. McCloskey and F. N. Trefethen (eds.), Baltimore: Johns Hopkins Press, 1954.
9. Henderson, A., and R. Schlaifer, "Mathematical Programming." *Harvard Business Review*, 32 (1954) 73-100.
10. Kemeney, J. G., Hazleton Mirkil, J. Laurie Snell, and Gerald L. Thompson, *Finite Mathematical Structures*, Englewood Cliffs, N. J.: Prentice-Hall, (1959).
11. Koopmans, T. C., *et al.*, *Activity Analysis of Production and Allocation*, New York: Wiley, 1951.
12. Kuhn, H. W., and A. W. Tucker (eds.), *Linear Inequalities and Related Systems*, Princeton, N.J.: Princeton University Press, 1956.
13. Metzger, R. W., *Elementary Mathematical Programming*, New York: Wiley, 1958. (Applications)
14. Reinfeld, N. V., and W. R. Vogel, *Mathematical Programming*, Englewood Cliffs, N. J.: 1958. (Applications)
15. Riley, Vera, and Saul I. Gass, *Bibliography on Linear Programming and Related Techniques*, Baltimore: Johns Hopkins Press, 1958.
16. Sasieni, Maurice, Arthur Yaspan, and Lawrence Friedman, "Allocation," chapter in *Operations Research, Methods and Problems*, New York: Wiley, 1959.
17. *Second Symposium on Linear Programming*, H. A. Antosiewicz (ed.), 2 vols., DCS Comptroller, USAF (1955).
18. Symonds, G. H., *Linear Programming: The Solution of Refinery Problems*, New York: Esso Standard Oil Co., 1955. (Applications)
19. Thrall, R. M., and Leonard Tornheim, *Vector Spaces and Matrices*, New York: Wiley, 1957.
20. Tucker, A. W., *Game Theory and Programming*, Stillwater, Okla.: Oklahoma State University, 1955.
21. Vajda, S., *The Theory of Games and Linear Programming*, New York: Wiley, 1956.
22. Vazsonyi, A., *Scientific Programming in Business and Industry*, New York: Wiley, 1958.

The following entry was discovered by the author after the manuscript was in proof:
23. Flood, M. M., "Linear Programming," chapter in *Operational Research in Practice*, Max Davies and Michel Verhulst (eds.), London: Pergamon Press, 1958.

Appendix I

Prerequisites

We summarize here the principal ideas and techniques, mostly from "linear algebra," actually used in the text. Details will be found in the auxiliary references listed at the end of this appendix and in many simular books as well. Paragraphs are numbered for ease of reference; thus 1.2 refers to paragraph 2 below on "Inequalities."

1. *Real Numbers.* We deal exclusively with real numbers, taking for granted a familiarity with the rules for addition, subtraction, multiplication, and division (except by zero).

2. *Inequalities.* If a and b are any real numbers then either a is less than b (written $a < b$), or $a = b$, or $b < a$. If $a < b$ and $b < c$ then $a < c$. If $a < b$ then we also say that b is greater than a, and write $b > a$. The notation $a \le b$ means that either $a < b$ or $a = b$, and one says that a is "less than or equal to b" or "not greater than b"; similarly for $a \ge b$. We write $-\infty < x < \infty$ (or $0 \le x < \infty$) to indicate that x can take on any real value (or any nonnegative real value).

Like an equality, an inequality is preserved under addition: if $a < b$ then $a + c < b + c$. An inequality is preserved under multiplication by a positive number but is reversed if the multiplier is negative: if $a < b$, $c > 0$, and $d < 0$, then $ac < bc$ but $ad > bd$.

Like an equation, an inequality containing a variable may be true for some values of the variable and false for others. If we wish to learn, for example, for which values of x it is true that $7x - 5 \ge 4x + 2$, we may add $5 - 4x$ to each side, getting $3x \ge 7$, and multiply by $\frac{1}{3}$, arriving at the clear-cut condition $x \ge \frac{7}{3}$; since the steps can be reversed, the latter inequality is equivalent to the original one.

3. *Absolute Value.* The absolute value, or modulus, of a number b is denoted by $|b|$ and is defined as follows: $|b| = b$ if $b \ge 0$, and $|b| = -b$ if $b < 0$. Clearly $|b| \ge 0$ and $|b| = 0$ if and only if $b = 0$. It can be shown that $|ab| = |a||b|$ and that

$$||a| - |b|| \le |a \pm b| \le |a| + |b|,$$

whichever sign is used in the middle term. It may be desired, for example, to estimate how large an expression such as $ax + by + cz$ can be under certain conditions on x, y, and z. One might know that $|x| \leq K$, $|y| \leq K$, and $|z| \leq K$; it would then follow that

$$|ax + by + cz| \leq |ax| + |by| + |cz| = |a||x| + |b||y| + |c||z|$$
$$\leq |a|K + |b|K + |c|K = (|a| + |b| + |c|)K.$$

4. Sets. The brief word "set" is used to denote any class, collection, or aggregate of objects treated as a single unit of thought. Thus one may speak of the set of positive integers, the set of points lying above a horizontal line in a plane, or the set of points lying either inside a circle or on its circumference. One writes $a \, \epsilon \, S$ or $a \, \epsilon' \, S$ to indicate respectively that the object a does or does not belong to the set S, that it is or is not an element of S.

As indicated by the examples just cited, a set S is often obtained by putting into S those elements having a certain property and rejecting those not having the property.

There are properties not possessed by any object for which they have meaning; there is no integer whose square is 3, nor any positive number whose square is negative. One says that the set corresponding to such a property is empty, or void, and calls it the null set.

The intersection of a family of sets consists of precisely those objects belonging to every member of the family.

5. Subsets. If every element of a set S is also an element of a set T then S is said to be a subset of T. The elements of T not in S form another subset of T that is often called the complement of S (relative to T) and denoted by S_T'. When it is perfectly evident what T is, one abbreviates S_T' to S'. For example, if T consists of a, b, c, d, and e, then the set S consisting of a, c, and d, and the set S' consisting of b and e are complementary subsets of T.

6. Ordered Sets; Indices. The elements a of a set S may occur in a prescribed order or sequence, so that S has a first element, a second element, a third, and so on. It is then natural and convenient to write a_1, a_2, a_3, and so on, and to call $(a_1, a_2, \cdots, a_n)$ an ordered n-tuple of elements of S (pair if $n = 2$, triple if $n = 3$).

The ordered n-tuple may also be denoted by (a_k) $(k = 1, \cdots, n)$, and its separate elements by a_k $(k = 1, \cdots, n)$; the variable subscript k is called an index, and the integers $1, \cdots, n$ are values of the index. Indices are sometimes written as superscripts; ordinarily it is evident from the context that no confusion with exponents is possible.

7. Mathematical Induction. Suppose that a set S has these two properties: (a) $1 \, \epsilon \, S$, and (b) for $k = 1, 2, 3, \cdots$, if $k \, \epsilon \, S$ then $k + 1 \, \epsilon \, S$. The fundamental principle of mathematical induction, which we accept here as an axiom or postulate, states that then each positive integer is an element of S.

This principle underlies a method of proving that a proposition P_n, depending for its meaning on the value of the positive integer n, is true for each value of n. The first step is to prove that P_1 is true. The second step is to prove that, for $k = 1, 2, 3, \cdots$, if P_k is true then P_{k+1} is true. One then concludes from the principle of induction (with S as the set of positive integers n for which P_n is true) that P_n is true for $n = 1, 2, 3, \cdots$. Examples will be found in many elementary or intermediate textbooks on algebra; see, for example, auxiliary reference [1] (pp. 11-14) or [4] (pp. 302-5).

8. *Recursive Definition.* Similar steps may be used to define a function $f(n)$ of a positive integral variable $n - 1, 2, 3, \cdots$. One first finds the value $f(1)$ of f when $n = 1$. Then, for $k = 1, 2, 3, \cdots$, one has means, when $f(1), f(2), \cdots$, $f(k)$ are known, to calculate $f(k + 1)$. Such a definition is called a recursive or an inductive definition. For example, the important factorial function $n!$ is defined as follows: $1! = 1$ and $(k + 1)! = (k!) (k + 1)$. One sees readily (and can prove at once by induction) that, for each value of n, $n! = 1 \cdot 2 \cdot \cdots, n$; it is reasonable and customary to define $0! = 1$.

9. *Sigma Notation.* We shall have frequent occasion to deal with sums such as $a_1 + \cdots + a_8$ or $b_1c_1 + \cdots + b_nc_n$. One usually designates such sums by using a subscript index to indicate a typical term, such as a_j ($j = 1, \cdots, 8$) or b_kc_k ($k = 1, \cdots, n$), and to prefix a Greek capital Σ with indication of the range of the index. For example,

$$\sum_{j=1}^{8} a_j = a_1 + \cdots + a_8$$

and

$$\sum_{k=1}^{n} b_kc_k = b_1c_1 + \cdots + b_nc_n.$$

When it is perfectly obvious what the index of summation is, one may omit it, writing, for example, $\Sigma_1^8 a_j$. If the range is also evident, one may write simply Σa_j. If, again, a quantity has several indices—say, a_{pqr}—and one wishes to sum over q only, and knows that $q = 1, \cdots, 3$, then

$$\Sigma_q a_{pqr} = \sum_{q=1}^{3} a_{pqr} = a_{p1r} + a_{p2r} + a_{p3r}.$$

10. *Row and Column Vectors; Scalars.* For our purposes a vector is defined to be an ordered n-tuple of real numbers, each element of the n-tuple being called a component of the vector. The components are always listed either in a horizontal row enclosed by brackets or in a vertical column enclosed by brackets; the vector is called a row vector or a column vector in the respective cases. A vector will be denoted by a Latin capital letter. If X is a row (or column) vector then the column (or row) vector with the same respective components is called the transpose of X and is denoted by X^t; as a consequence, $(X^t)^t = X$ for any vector X. If X denotes a vector, it will be stated explicitly or implied clearly by the context whether X is a row or a column vector.

A row vector will be displayed as

$$X = [x_1, \cdots, x_n] = [x_j] \qquad (j = 1, \cdots, n).$$

Then the transpose of X will be the column vector

$$X^t = [x_1, \cdots, x_n]^t = \begin{bmatrix} x_1 \\ \vdots \\ x_n \end{bmatrix}.$$

Since it is typographically inconvenient to display column vectors frequently, a column vector will often be represented as the transpose of a row vector.

It is customary in this context to call a real number a scalar. Although the scalar c, the row vector $[c]$, and the column vector $[c]^t$ are conceptually distinct, both $[c]$ and $[c]^t$ have properties indistinguishable from those of c, and we shall therefore identify the three for practical purposes; then c^t makes sense, and $c^t = c$.

We define $X = Y$ to be true when and only when X and Y are either both row vectors or both column vectors, they have the same number of components —say, n—and, for $j = 1, \cdots, n$, $x_j = y_j$.

It is very convenient to accept a systematic ambiguity in terminology, whereby we speak of the point X or of the vector X; the point P whose coordinates are the components of X is in fact the terminal point of the vector $\overrightarrow{OP}$ from the origin to P, so that the vector $X = \overrightarrow{OP}$ is the position vector with respect to the origin O of the point X.

11. *Addition of Vectors.* Given vectors $X = [x_j]$ and $Y = [y_j]$ $(j = 1, \cdots, n)$, their sum is defined to be

$$X + Y = [x_j + y_j] \qquad (j = 1, \cdots, n);$$

we also define $X^t + Y^t$ to be $(X + Y)^t$. It is evident that

$$X + Y = Y + X$$

and that

$$(X + Y) + Z = X + (Y + Z),$$

and similarly for column vectors. The vector X with $x_j = 0$ $(j = 1, \cdots, n)$ will be called the zero vector and denoted simply by 0. Clearly $X + 0 = X$. If $X = [x_j]$ and we define $- X$ to be $[- x_j]$ $(j = 1, \cdots, n)$ then

$$X + (- X) = 0.$$

We abbreviate $X + (- Y)$ to $X - Y$ and speak of subtracting Y from X. Similarly for column vectors.

12. *Multiplication of a Vector by a Scalar.* Given a vector X and a scalar a we define $aX = Xa$ to be

$$[ax_j] \qquad (j = 1, \cdots, n),$$

and also define aX^t to be $(aX)^t$. It is evident that if $a = + 1$ then $aX = X$, if $a = - 1$ then $aX = - X$ $(cf.$ 1. 11), and if $a = 0$ then $aX = 0$. The operation of multiplying a vector by a scalar obeys the following laws:

$$(a + b)X = aX + bX,$$
$$a(X + Y) = aX + aY,$$

and

$$a(bX) = (ab)X.$$

Similarly throughout for column vectors. *Examples*:

$$2[3,c] - 3[a, -1] = [6, 2c] + [-3a, 3] = [6 - 3a, 2c + 3],$$

$$a\begin{bmatrix} 2 \\ -1 \end{bmatrix} + b\begin{bmatrix} c \\ 0 \end{bmatrix} - 2\begin{bmatrix} 3 \\ -1 \end{bmatrix} = \begin{bmatrix} 2a + bc - 6 \\ -a + 2 \end{bmatrix}.$$

13. *Scalar or Dot Product of Two Vectors.* With each pair of n-component vectors X and Y of the same kind there is associated a scalar, called the scalar or dot product of X and Y, denoted by $X \cdot Y$, and defined to be

$$\sum_{j=1}^{n} x_j y_j;$$

thus $$X^t \cdot Y^t = X \cdot Y.$$

The scalar product has the following properties:

$$X \cdot Y = Y \cdot X, \qquad X \cdot (Y + Z) = X \cdot Y + X \cdot Z,$$

and $$(aX) \cdot Y = a(X \cdot Y) = X \cdot (aY);$$

similarly for column vectors. *Example*:

$$\begin{bmatrix} 2 \\ a \\ -1 \end{bmatrix} \cdot \begin{bmatrix} 2 \\ 3 \\ b \end{bmatrix} = [2, a, -1] \cdot [2, 3, b] = 2 \cdot 2 + a \cdot 3 + (-1) \cdot b = 3a - b + 4.$$

Observing that

$$X \cdot X = \Sigma_j x_j^2 > 0$$

unless $X = 0$, we may define the length of X to be

$$|X| = \sqrt{X \cdot X}.$$

We have little interest here in the geometric properties of the scalar product, and have introduced it primarily for notational convenience.

14. *Linear Spaces.* A real linear (or vector) space consists of (a) a set of objects, usually called vectors, (b) an operation of adding vectors, defined in such a way as to have the properties mentioned for $X + Y$ in I.11, and (c) an operation of multiplying a vector by a scalar (real number), defined so as to have the properties mentioned for aX in I.12.

The set of all n-component row vectors, with addition and multiplication by a scalar defined as in I.11 and I.12, is an example of a real n-dimensional (see I.23) vector space and is in a quite precise sense the prototype of all such spaces. Similarly for the set of all n-component column vectors; see also I.18 below.

With the definitions of scalar product and length in I.13, our linear space becomes a metric linear space, in that calculation of distances and angles becomes possible. For dimension 2 we have essentially a plane with a fixed system of rectangular cartesian coordinates; one ordinarily writes (x,y) instead of $[x_1, x_2]$. If $n = 3$, we have essentially a fixed rectangular cartesian coordinate system in 3-dimensional space, and one usually writes (x, y, z) instead of $[x_1, x_2, x_3]$. Since the n-dimensional metric space of row vectors is an example of Euclidean n-space and is the prototype of all such spaces, we may for our purposes simply call it Euclidean n-space and denote it by E_n. It is desirable to keep the n-dimensional metric linear space of column vectors conceptually distinct from E_n (although they are in a certain precise sense entirely equivalent), and we therefore denote the space of n-component column vectors by E_n^t. If X is a row vector then

$$X \in E_n \qquad \text{and} \qquad X^t \in E_n^t;$$

if Y is a column vector then

$$Y \in E_n^t \qquad \text{and} \qquad Y^t \in E_n.$$

15. *Functions and Functionals.* A real-valued function f defined on a subset S of E_n may be regarded as a function $f(x_1, \cdots, x_n)$ of the coordinates of a variable point X of S, or as a function $f(X)$ of the position vector X of the variable point. In the theory of linear spaces it is usual to call a scalar-valued function a functional; thus $f(X)$ is a functional.

If f is sufficiently well-behaved (in a sense into which we need not go here) and c is a suitable fixed real number, then the set of all points X such that $f(X) = c$ will constitute a surface. Such a surface is called a level surface of f or, in the plane, a level curve or contour line. For example, if $c > 0$ then the set of all $X \in E_3$ such that $x^2 + y^2 + z^2 = c^2$ is a sphere with center at the origin and radius c; thus the level surfaces of $f(X) = x^2 + y^2 + z^2$ consist of spheres with center at the origin.

16. *Linear Functionals.* A functional f defined on a linear space is said to be linear if for any vectors X and Y and scalars a and b it is true that

$$f(aX + bY) = af(X) + bf(Y).$$

An equivalent requirement is that f be both additive, in the sense that

$$f(X + Y) = f(X) + f(Y),$$

and homogeneous in the sense that

$$f(aX) = af(X).$$

It can be shown that f is linear on E_n if and only if there exist constants a_j ($j = 1, \cdots, n$), depending on f but not on X, such that if $X = [x_j]$ then

$$f(X) = \sum_{j=1}^{n} a_j x_j.$$

In E_3, for example, f is linear if and only if it is of the form $ax + by + cz$. In E_2 the level curves $ax + by = c$ of a linear functional are straight lines; in E_3 the level surfaces $ax + by + cz = d$ of a linear functional are planes. In E_n it is usual to speak of the level surfaces of a linear functional as hyperplanes or merely planes.

17. *Linear Inequalities; Half-spaces.* Simple geometric arguments in E_2 show that a point $X = [x_0, y_0]$ not on the line $ax + by = c$ will lie on one side or the other of the line according as $ax_0 + by_0 > c$ or $< c$. (See Fig. 3, p. 7.) In E_3 and in E_n generally, it can be shown that if f is linear then the sets defined by $f(X) > c$ or $f(X) < c$ consist of all points on one side or the other of the plane $f(X) = c$. It is natural (even if $n = 2$) to call these sets open half-spaces. Similarly, the sets $f(X) \geq c$ or $f(X) \leq c$ consist of open half-spaces with the bounding plane adjoined, and may therefore be called closed half-spaces.

18. Duality. It is possible to make the set of all linear functionals on E_n into a linear space by suitable definitions of adding two functionals and of multiplying a functional by a scalar. One simply agrees that $f + g$ shall have for each $X \epsilon E_n$ the value $f(X) + g(X)$ and that if c is a scalar then cf shall have for each $X \epsilon E_n$ the value $cf(X)$; it is readily seen that $f + g$ and cf are indeed linear functionals. The effect of these definitions is that if $f(X) = \Sigma_j a_j x_j$ and $g(X) = \Sigma_j b_j x_j$ then

$$(f + g)(X) = \Sigma_j (a_j + b_j)x_j$$

and
$$(cf)(X) = \Sigma_j (ca_j)x_j.$$

With these definitions, the linear space of all linear functionals on E_n is called the space dual to E_n. It can be shown that the dual of E_n can be identified with E_n^t, and vice versa; in other words, the space E_n of n-component row vectors and the space E_n^t of n-component column vectors are dual to each other. When multiplication of matrices has been defined, in I.26 below, it will turn out that every linear functional $f(X)$ on E_n can be written as the matrix product XA for some $A \epsilon E_n^t$, while every linear functional on E_n^t can be written as the matrix product AX for some $A \epsilon E_n$.

The foregoing remarks will supply at least a partial motivation, we hope, for the uses made in the text and in Appendix II of the terminology of duality. For the sake of completeness we mention one further fact, not used in the text; readers finding it puzzling can simply ignore it. The spaces E_n and E_n^t are both self-dual, in the sense that for each linear functional f on E_n (or on E_n^t) there exists a unique element $A \epsilon E_n$ (or $A^t \epsilon E_n^t$) such that, for each $X \epsilon E_n$ (or $X^t \epsilon E_n^t$) it is true that $f(X) = A \cdot X$ (or $f(X^t) = A^t \cdot X^t$), where the dot indicates the dot product of I.13.

19. Linear Combinations of Vectors. Let X_α ($\alpha = 1, \cdots, q$) be q given vectors with each $X_\alpha \epsilon E_n$. If a_α are scalars then

$$Y = \sum_{\alpha=1}^{q} a_\alpha X_\alpha$$

is a vector in E_n that is said to be a linear combination of the vectors X_α. Similarly,

$$Y^t = \sum_{\alpha=1}^{q} a_\alpha X_\alpha^t \epsilon E_n^t.$$

The scalars a_α are called coefficients of combination. For example, for $j = 1$,

$\cdots$, n let B_j denote the vector having each component zero except the jth, which has the value 1; then

$$X = [x_1, \cdots, x_n] = \sum_{j=1}^{n} x_j B_j.$$

20. Subspaces. It is of interest to keep q and the vectors X_α fixed and to allow the scalars a_α to vary in such a way that each may take on any real value.

First, let $q = 1$ and suppose that $X_1 \neq 0$. The vectors $Y = a_1 X_1$ are indicated at the left in the diagram of Fig. 6, with points specified for $a_1 = 0$, $\frac{1}{2}$, 1, 2, and $- 1$. For each real value of a_1 there is a unique point on the line containing the points 0 and X_1, and vice versa—for each point on the line there is a unique corresponding number a_1.

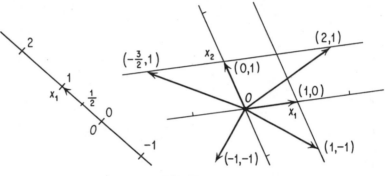

FIGURE 6

Now let $q = 2$ and suppose that X_1 and X_2 are two vectors such that neither is a multiple of the other. Then, as the numbers a_α ($\alpha = 1, 2$) vary, the point $a_1 X_1 + a_2 X_2$ fills up the plane determined by O, X_1, and X_2. On the right in Fig. 6 a few points have been indicated, along with the accompanying ordered pairs (a_1, a_2).

If $q = 3$ it is possible to illustrate similarly the set of all

$$Y = \sum_{\alpha=1}^{3} a_\alpha X_\alpha.$$

Unless the vectors X_α ($\alpha = 1, 2, 3$) lie in a plane, Y can be any point in E_3.

If $q > 3$ then it is not possible, except in special cases, to illustrate visually in a similar way the set of all linear combinations of X_α ($\alpha = 1, \cdots, q$). The algebraic situation is fundamentally unchanged, however, and geometric language enables us to express various relationships in a suggestive way.

Let S denote the set of *all* linear combinations of X_α ($\alpha = 1, \cdots, q$). If

$$Y = \Sigma a_\alpha X_\alpha \in S$$

and c is a scalar then

$$cY = \Sigma c a_\alpha X_\alpha \in S.$$

If also

$$Z = \Sigma \, b_\alpha X_\alpha \in S$$

then

$$Y + Z = \Sigma \, (a_\alpha + b_\alpha) X_\alpha \in S.$$

More generally, if

$$Y_\mu \, (\mu = 1, \cdots, m) \in S$$

then any linear combination

$$Z = \sum_{\mu=1}^{m} c_\mu Y_\mu$$

is an element of S, for if

$$Y_\mu = \sum_{\alpha=1}^{q} a_{\mu\alpha} X_\alpha$$

then

$$Z = \sum_{\mu=1}^{m} c_\mu \left[\sum_{\alpha=1}^{q} a_{\mu\alpha} X_\alpha \right] = \sum_{\alpha=1}^{q} \left[\sum_{\mu=1}^{m} c_\mu a_{\mu\alpha} \right] X_\alpha.$$

Thus all the operations of vector algebra, when performed upon elements of S, yield elements of S. In this sense S is itself a linear space; since every element of S is in E_n, S is called a subspace of E_n and is said to be generated or spanned by the vectors X_α. The "largest" subspace of E_n is E_n itself. It is important to recognize that every subspace of E_n contains the zero vector of E_n. The zero vector taken by itself generates a subspace whose only element is the zero vector; this subspace is the "smallest" subspace of E_n. In E_n^t or in any linear space the zero vector has these properties.

21. *Nonnegative Linear Combinations.* If $Y = \Sigma_\alpha \, a_\alpha X_\alpha$ and the a_α are subjected to the restrictions $a_\alpha \geq 0$ then the set T of all linear combinations of X_α subject to these restrictions is not a linear space; multiplication by the scalar -1, for example, is not possible within T. In the diagram of I.20, when $q = 1$ the set T consists of the ray or half-line of points above and to the left of 0 (including 0); when $q = 2$, the set T consists of the quadrant of points that are both above the line $0X_1$ and to the right of the line $0X_2$ or on one of those half-lines (including 0). In the general case the set T is usually called the positive cone of the subspace generated by the X_α.

22. *Linear Dependence and Independence.* Let $X_\alpha \in E_n$ $(\alpha = 1, \cdots, q)$. A vector $Y \in E_n$ is said to depend on the set X_α if and only if it is a linear combination, $Y = \Sigma_\alpha \, a_\alpha X_\alpha$, of the vectors X_α (see I.18); in other words, if and only if it is in the subspace of E_n generated by the vectors X_α (see I.20, last paragraph). The set X_α is said to be a dependent set if one of the vectors depends on the others. In I.20, for example, in the case $q = 2$, the vectors X_α are dependent if and only if one is a multiple of the other.

If the set X_α is dependent and

$$X_{\alpha_0} = \sum_{\alpha \neq \alpha_0} a_\alpha X_\alpha$$

then $\qquad\qquad \Sigma_\alpha \, a_\alpha X_\alpha = 0 \qquad$ (with $a_{\alpha_0} = -1$);

there exist, therefore, constants a_α, *not all zero*, such that

$$\Sigma_\alpha \, a_\alpha X_\alpha = 0.$$

The converse is clearly true, for if

$$\Sigma_\alpha \, a_\alpha X_\alpha = 0$$

with, say, $a_{\alpha_0} \neq 0$, then one can solve for X_{α_0}, thus expressing it as a linear combination of the others.

The set X_α is said to be independent if it is not dependent. Thus the set X_α is independent if and only if

$$\Sigma_\alpha \, a_\alpha X_\alpha = 0$$

implies that

$$a_\alpha = 0 \qquad (\alpha = 1, \, \cdots, \, q);$$

the *only* way, therefore, of expressing the zero vector as a linear combination of the vectors X_α is to take all the coefficients of combination equal to zero. In I.20, for example, in the case $q = 2$, the vectors X_α are independent (neither is a multiple of the other) and therefore $a_1 X_1 + a_2 X_2 = 0$ is not possible unless $a_1 = a_2 = 0$.

It is easy to see that any subset of an independent set is itself an independent set, while any set having a dependent subset is itself dependent.

23. Basis and Dimension. Suppose that vectors X_α $(\alpha = 1, \, \cdots, \, q)$ generate a subspace S of E_n. The same subspace can be generated equally well by other sets of vectors in it. If the set Y_β $(\beta = 1, \, \cdots, \, r)$ generates a subspace S and the set Y_β is an independent set, then one calls Y_β a basis of S. It can be shown that any other basis for S will also contain r vectors; the integer r is called the dimension of S. The vectors B_j $(j = 1, \, \cdots, \, n)$ of I.19 are independent and generate E_n; this is why we say that E_n is n-dimensional. In Fig. 6 of I.20 the vector X_1, on the left, generates the one-dimensional space consisting of the line containing the points 0 and X_1, while on the right the vectors X_1 and X_2 are independent and generate the two-dimensional space consisting of the plane containing the points 0, X_1, and X_2.

The essential property of a basis Y_β $(\beta = 1, \, \cdots, \, r)$ of a subspace S is this: If $Z \, \epsilon \, S$ then there exist *unique* scalars z_β such that

$$Z = \Sigma_\beta \, z_\beta Y_\beta.$$

The scalars exist because the vectors Y_β generate S. If also

$$Z = \Sigma_\beta \, z'_\beta Y_\beta$$

then, by subtraction,

$$0 = \Sigma_\beta (z_\beta - z'_\beta) Y_\beta$$

and it follows, since the vectors Y_β are independent, that

$$z_\beta - z'_\beta = 0.$$

24. Matrices. Let X_α $(\alpha = 1, \cdots, m)$ be an ordered m-tuple of n-component row vectors. If for each α, $X_\alpha = [x_{\alpha j}]$ $(j = 1, \cdots, n)$, then the index α indicates the vector X_α and the index j indicates that $x_{\alpha j}$ is the jth component of X_α. If the rows of components of the X_α are written down in order, starting with X_1, and with the respective components of $X_{\alpha+1}$ directly under those of X_α $(\alpha = 1, \cdots, m - 1)$, then the result is a rectangular array of m rows with n real numbers in a row. Any such rectangular array (however obtained) will be called an $m \times n$ matrix. If $m = 2$ and $n = 3$, for example, then

$$[x_{\alpha j}] = \begin{bmatrix} x_{11} & x_{12} & x_{13} \\ x_{21} & x_{22} & x_{23} \end{bmatrix}.$$

The matrix $[x_{\alpha j}]$ consists at the same time of n column vectors, each with m components. In the example, for instance, the third column vector is $[x_{13}, x_{23}]^t$. From this point of view, $x_{\alpha j}$ is the αth component of the jth column vector.

A row vector with p components is a $1 \times p$ matrix, while a column vector with q components is a $q \times 1$ matrix.

Latin capitals are used as abbreviations for matrices as well as for vectors; the nature of each such symbol may be evident from the context and is clearly displayed, in any event, by the definition of the symbol.

If A is an $m \times n$ matrix then its transpose, A^t, is an $n \times m$ matrix whose columns are the transposes of the respective rows of A; if

$$A = [x_{\alpha j}]$$

with $\alpha = 1, \cdots, m$ and $j = 1, \cdots, n$ then

$$A^t = [y_{k\beta}]$$

with $k = 1, \cdots, n$ and $\beta = 1, \cdots, m$ and, for each pair of indices k, β,

$$y_{k\beta} = x_{\beta k}.$$

A matrix is said to be square if $m = n$, in other words, if it has the same number of rows and columns. If this number is n then the matrix is said to be of order n. A square matrix A is said to be symmetric if $A^t = A$, and to be anti-symmetric or skew symmetric, or merely skew, if $A^t = -A$.

An important square matrix has the vectors B_j of I.19 as its row vectors (and the vectors B_j^t as its column vectors). For reasons to be given soon (see I.26, end), this matrix is called the nth-order identity matrix. It is denoted by I_n or simply by I, and the special symbol δ_{ij} (Kronecker's delta) is used for its elements. Thus

$$I_n = [\delta_{ij}]$$

where, for $i, j = 1, \cdots, n$, $\delta_{ij} = 1$ if $i = j$, and $\delta_{ij} = 0$ if $i \neq j$. Note that

$$\Sigma_j \, \delta_{ij} b_j = b_i.$$

If A is a square matrix, $A = [a_{ij}]$ with $i, j = 1, \cdots, n$, then the (principal) diagonal of A consists of those elements a_{ij} having $i = j$. Thus I has every element on the diagonal equal to one and all others equal to zero.

25. *Linear Operations on Matrices.* Matrices $A = [a_{hi}]$, with $h = 1, \cdots,$ m and $i = 1, \cdots, n$, and $B = [b_{jk}]$, with $j = 1, \cdots, p$ and $k = 1, \cdots, q$ are equal (written $A = B$) if and only if $m = p$, $n = q$, and, for $h = 1, \cdots, m$ and $i = 1,$ $\cdots, n$, $a_{hi} = b_{hi}$. A zero matrix has each element equal to zero and is denoted by 0, the number of rows and columns being evident from the context.

The sum of A and B is defined if and only if $m = p$ and $n = q$. If $m = p$ and $n = q$ then

$$A + B = C = [c_{hi}]$$

where, for $h = 1, \cdots, m$ and $i = 1, \cdots, n$,

$$c_{hi} = a_{hi} + b_{hi}.$$

It is easy to prove that

$$A + (B + C) = (A + B) + C, \qquad\qquad A + 0 = A,$$
$$A + (-A) = 0 \qquad (\text{where} - [a_{hi}] = [-a_{hi}],$$

and

$$A + B = B + A.$$

If $A = [a_{hi}]$ and c is a scalar then

$$cA = [ca_{hi}];$$

if $c = 1$ then $cA = A$, if $c = 0$ then $cA = 0$, and if $c = -1$ then $cA = -A$. It is also true that

$$b(cA) = (bc)A,$$
$$(b + c)A = bA + cA,$$
$$c(A + B) = cA + cB,$$
$$(A + B)^t = A^t + B^t,$$

and

$$(cA)^t = cA^t.$$

26. *Multiplication of Matrices.* Suppose that we wish to calculate the n components of a linear combination

$$Y = \sum_{\alpha=1}^{m} a_\alpha X_\alpha$$

of the row vectors X_α of a matrix $X = [x_{\alpha j}]$. The jth component is clearly

$$\sum_{\alpha=1}^{m} a_\alpha x_{\alpha j},$$

and

$$Y = \left[\sum_{\alpha=1}^{m} a_\alpha x_{\alpha j} \right].$$

This calculation can be indicated conveniently by defining an m-component row vector $A = [a_\alpha]$ and writing $Y = AX$ (A to the left and X to the right); for example, if X is a 2×3 matrix then A will be a two-component row vector and Y will be a three-component row vector, calculated as follows:

$$Y = AX = [a_1, a_2] \begin{bmatrix} x_{11} & x_{12} & x_{13} \\ x_{21} & x_{22} & x_{23} \end{bmatrix} = [a_1 x_{11} + a_2 x_{21}, \ a_1 x_{12} + a_2 x_{22}, \ a_1 x_{13} + a_2 x_{23}].$$

It is important to recognize that the jth component

$$y_j = \Sigma_\alpha \ a_\alpha x_{\alpha j}$$

of Y is the same linear combination of the jth components of X_α (appearing in the jth column of X) as Y itself is of X_α; thus we multiply the successive elements across the row of A (on the left) by the respective elements down the column of X (on the right) and add in order to get a column of the result.

Similarly, if we wish to calculate the m components of a linear combination

$$U = \sum_{j=1}^{n} b_j U_j$$

of the column vectors U_j of a matrix $U = [u_{\alpha j}]$, it is convenient to define an n-component column vector $B = [b_j]^t$ and to write $V = UB$ (U to the left and B to the right); for example, if U is a 2×3 matrix then B will be a three-component column vector and V will be a two-component column vector, calculated as follows:

$$V = UB = \begin{bmatrix} u_{11} & u_{12} & u_{13} \\ u_{21} & u_{22} & u_{23} \end{bmatrix} \begin{bmatrix} b_1 \\ b_2 \\ b_3 \end{bmatrix} = \begin{bmatrix} u_{11}b_1 + u_{12}b_2 + u_{13}b_3 \\ u_{21}b_1 + u_{22}b_2 + u_{23}b_3 \end{bmatrix} = \begin{bmatrix} {}_j\Sigma_1^3 \ u_{1j}b_j \\ {}_j\Sigma_1^3 \ u_{2j}b_j \end{bmatrix}.$$

Here the αth component $v_\alpha = \Sigma_j \ u_{\alpha j} b_j$ of V is the same linear combination of the αth components of U_j (appearing in the αth row of U) as V itself is of U_j; thus we again multiply the successive elements across the row of U (on the left) by the respective elements down the column of B (on the right) and add to get a row of the result.

If we wish several linear combinations of the row vectors of X, with their components arranged as the rows of a matrix, then there will be a separate and respective row of A for each of the desired linear combinations. If we wish several linear combinations of the column vectors of U, with their components arranged as the columns of a matrix, then there will be a separate and respective column of B for each of the desired linear combinations.

The expressions AX and UB are instances of the product of two matrices. We now turn to the general definition. Let $A = [a_{hi}]$, with $h = 1, \cdots, m$ and $i = 1, \cdots, n$, be an $m \times n$ matrix and let $B = [b_{jk}]$, with $j = 1, \cdots, p$ and $k = 1, \cdots, q$, be a $p \times q$ matrix. Then the matrix product AB (in that order) is defined if and only if $n = p$; that is, if the number of columns of A is equal to the number of rows of B. If $n = p$ then the product AB is an $m \times q$ matrix $C = [c_{hk}]$, with $h = 1, \cdots, m$ and $k = 1, \cdots, q$, such that, for each value of h and of k,

$$c_{hk} = \sum_{j=1}^{n} a_{hj} b_{jk}.$$

Thus the element in the hth row and kth column of C is obtained by multiplying the successive elements across the hth row of A (on the left) by the respective elements down the kth column of B (on the right) and adding.

In the first example above we had a 1×2 matrix A and a 2×3 matrix X and obtained a 1×3 matrix $Y = AX$; in the second we had a 2×3 matrix U and a 3×1 matrix B and obtained a 2×1 matrix $V = UB$. If X and Y are two n-component row (or column) vectors then $X \cdot Y = XY^t$ (or $X \cdot Y = X^t Y$). *Examples:*

$$[x \ \ y] \begin{bmatrix} a \\ b \end{bmatrix} = ax + by, \qquad \begin{bmatrix} a \\ b \end{bmatrix} [x \ \ y] = \begin{bmatrix} ax & ay \\ bx & by \end{bmatrix},$$

$$\begin{bmatrix} a_{11} & a_{12} & \cdots & a_{1n} \\ a_{21} & a_{22} & \cdots & a_{2n} \\ & & & \\ a_{m1} & a_{m2} & \cdots & a_{mn} \end{bmatrix} \begin{bmatrix} x_1 \\ x_2 \\ \vdots \\ x_n \end{bmatrix} = \begin{bmatrix} a_{11} x_1 + a_{12} x_2 + \cdots + a_{1n} x_n \\ a_{21} x_1 + a_{22} x_2 + \cdots + a_{2n} x_n \\ \\ a_{m1} x_1 + a_{m2} x_2 + \quad + a_{mn} x_n \end{bmatrix}$$

It may happen that AB is defined while BA is not; even if both are defined it will be exceptional, as indicated in the first two examples just displayed, for AB to equal BA. It is true, when the products mentioned are defined, that

$$(AB)^t = B^t A^t,$$
$$A(BC) = (AB)C,$$
$$A(B + C) = AB + AC,$$

and
$$(A + B)C = AC + BC.$$

If c is a scalar then

$$(cA)B = c(AB) = A(cB).$$

If 0 is a zero matrix having in each case the appropriate respective number of columns or rows then $0A = 0$ and $A0 = 0$. If I is the identity matrix of the appropriate respective order then $IA = A$ and $AI = A$.

If we denote by Y the $m \times 1$ column vector on the right in the last displayed example and by A the matrix of coefficients then the equation may be written $Y = AX$. If $X = BZ$ then

$$Y = A(BZ) = (AB)Z = CZ$$

with $C = AB$; instead, therefore, of first calculating X from Z by means of B and then Y from X by means of A, one may first calculate AB and then use it to calculate Y directly from Z.

27. *Products of Partitioned Matrices.* If matrices are decomposed, figuratively speaking, by means of some horizontal lines between rows and some vertical lines between columns, then, if the submatrices of the respective matrices have the appropriate numbers of columns and rows, multiplication of the matrices can be performed as though the submatrices were elements of matrices. Although this idea is exceedingly simple, an adequate detailed statement would require considerable space; see the auxiliary references at the end of this appendix as follows: [1] pp. 218ff., [2] pp. 77 ff., [3] pp. 29-30, or [4] pp. 63 ff. *Example:*

$$\begin{bmatrix} a_{11} & a_{12} & \vdots & a_{13} \\ a_{21} & a_{22} & \vdots & a_{23} \\ \cdots & \cdots & \cdots \\ a_{31} & a_{32} & \vdots & a_{33} \end{bmatrix} \begin{bmatrix} y_{11} & y_{12} \\ y_{21} & y_{22} \\ \cdots \\ y_{31} & y_{32} \end{bmatrix} = \begin{bmatrix} a_{11}y_{11}+a_{12}y_{21}+a_{13}y_{31} & a_{11}y_{12}+a_{12}y_{22}+a_{13}y_{32} \\ a_{21}y_{11}+a_{22}y_{21}+a_{23}y_{31} & a_{21}y_{12}+a_{22}y_{22}+a_{23}y_{32} \\ a_{31}y_{11}+a_{32}y_{21}+a_{33}y_{31} & a_{31}y_{12}+a_{32}y_{22}+a_{33}y_{32} \end{bmatrix}$$

with
$$A = \begin{bmatrix} a_{11} & a_{12} \\ a_{21} & a_{22} \end{bmatrix}, \qquad B = \begin{bmatrix} a_{13} \\ a_{23} \end{bmatrix}, \qquad C = [a_{31} \quad a_{32}],$$

$$D = [a_{33}], \qquad Y = \begin{bmatrix} y_{11} & y_{12} \\ y_{21} & y_{22} \end{bmatrix}, \qquad \text{and} \qquad Z = [y_{31} \quad y_{32}],$$

we have, as may be verified by direct calculation,

$$\begin{bmatrix} A & B \\ C & D \end{bmatrix} \begin{bmatrix} Y \\ Z \end{bmatrix} = \begin{bmatrix} AY + BZ \\ CY + DZ \end{bmatrix}$$

28. *The Row Space of a Matrix; Row Operations.* The m row vectors of an $m \times n$ matrix X (*cf.* I.24) generate a subspace R of E_n (*cf.* I.20). This subspace is called the row space of X. (The column vectors generate a subspace of E_m^t called the column space of X. Our discussion can be modified to apply to it, but we do not use this idea here.) As seen in I.26, the effect of multiplying X on the left by a $1 \times m$ matrix (row vector) A is to produce a vector that is a linear combination of the row vectors of X and therefore lies in R. The effect of multiplying X on the left by a $p \times m$ matrix Z is to produce a $p \times n$ matrix ZX in which each row, as just seen, lies in R. The row space of ZX is therefore a subspace of the row space of X. Let us now specialize Z by insisting that Z be square ($m \times m$) and that its m rows be linearly independent m-component vectors (*cf.* I.22). It can be shown that if Z is of order m then this last condition— in technical language, that Z be nonsingular—is necessary and sufficient in order that the row spaces of X and ZX be identical.

It can also be shown that the same effect can be produced by performing on X a selected sequence of the following three operations: (a) interchanging two rows, (b) multiplying a row by a scalar, and (c) adding to one row any linear combination of the other rows. These operations are called row operations on X.

The principal use made of this idea in the text occurs when we have a matrix $X = [x_{\alpha j}]$ in which there is a particular element $x_{\alpha_0 j_0}$—often called the pivotal element—which is not zero, and we wish to obtain unity in that position and zero in all other positions in the j_0th column. The unity will result when the α_0th row is divided by $x_{\alpha_0 j_0}$. In order then to produce a zero in the α', j_0 position, we merely multiply the new α_0th row by $-x_{\alpha' j_0}$ and add to the α'th row.

In the following example we have arbitrarily chosen $x_{23} = 2$ as the pivotal element.

$$\begin{bmatrix} 2 & 3 & -4 & 2 \\ -1 & 0 & 2 & 3 \\ 3 & -1 & -2 & 1 \end{bmatrix}, \quad \begin{bmatrix} 2 & 3 & -4 & 2 \\ -\frac{1}{2} & 0 & 1 & \frac{3}{2} \\ 3 & -1 & -2 & 1 \end{bmatrix}, \quad \begin{bmatrix} 0 & 3 & 0 & 8 \\ -\frac{1}{2} & 0 & 1 & \frac{3}{2} \\ 2 & -1 & 0 & 4 \end{bmatrix}.$$

Starting with the matrix on the left, we divided the second row by 2 to obtain the second matrix, with 1 in the second row and third column. In that matrix the second row was then multiplied by 4 and added to the first, and by 2 and added to the third. In the final matrix, as desired, the third column has 1 in the second row and zero elsewhere.

Those readers familiar with the method of elimination for solving linear algebraic equations will recognize the equivalence of that process with the one just used; the latter is a critical step in the matrix formulation of Gauss' method of elimination.

29. *Inverse Matrix; Row Operations on the Identity.* If A and B are square matrices of order n, and $BA = I_n$, then it can be shown that B is uniquely determined by A and also that $AB = I_n$. The matrix B is called the inverse of A and is customarily denoted by A^{-1}; of course, then $A = B^{-1}$ also. In order that A have an inverse in this sense it is necessary and sufficient that A be non-singular in the sense of I.28; the same is then true of A^{-1}.

We saw in I.28 that the effect of multiplying A on the left by a nonsingular matrix B was to carry out a suitable sequence of row operations on A; we can therefore, if A is nonsingular, produce I from A by carrying out certain row operations on A. Now A is equal to IA always, whence $BA = (BI)A$. Since B is to the left of I it follows that if $B = A^{-1}$ and we carry out on I itself exactly those row operations, indicated by B, which reduce A to I, then the resulting matrix BI will be an explicit expression for A^{-1}.

Auxiliary References

1. Birkhoff, S., and G. MacLane, *A Survey of Modern Algebra* (rev. ed.), New York: Macmillan, 1953.
2. Hohn, F. E., *Elementary Matrix Algebra*, New York: Macmillan, 1958.
3. MacDuffee, C. C., *Vectors and Matrices* (Carus Mathematical Monograph No. 7, rev. ed.), Menasha, Wis.: Mathematical Association of America, 1949.
4. Thrall, R. M., and L. Tornheim, *Vector Spaces and Matrices*, New York: Wiley, 1957.

Appendix II

Theorems on Existence and Duality

It is our purpose in this appendix to outline a proof of the theorems on existence and duality cited in Section 3. We follow [12] (papers 1 and 4), where complete details may be found along with extensive further results not needed here.

We are concerned with a matrix $A = [a_{\alpha j}]$ ($\alpha = 1, \cdots, m; j = 1, \cdots, n$), and shall denote by A_j the vector appearing in the jth column of A. The symbols U and V will denote row vectors with the number of components (usually m) indicated by the context; X and Y will denote column vectors with the appropriate number of components (usually n). The transpose of a matrix M is denoted by M^t; for the meaning of inequalities involving matrices see p. 4 (top). Several lemmas will be needed.

Lemma 1 ([12] p. 5). *For each A there exist U and X such that $UA \geq 0$, $X \geq 0$, $AX = 0$, and $UA_1 + x_1 > 0$.*

If $n = 1$ and $A_1 \neq 0$ take $U = A_1^t$ and $X = 0$. If $A_1 = 0$ take $U = 0$, $x_1 = 1$, and $x_{j'} = 0$ ($j' = 2, \cdots, n$).

Assume now, as an inductive hypothesis, that the lemma is true if A has n columns ($n > 1$). Let A have n columns and let U and X be specific vectors meeting the conditions of the lemma. Then consider $\bar{A} = [A, A_{n+1}]$. If $UA_{n+1} \geq 0$ then we take $\bar{U} = U$ and $\bar{X} = [X^t, 0]^t$, verifying easily that $\bar{U}$ and $\bar{X}$ meet the requirements of the lemma. We are left with the case $UA_{n+1} < 0$.

For $j = 1, \cdots, n$ define
$$\lambda_j = -\frac{UA_j}{UA_{n+1}}$$
and observe that each $\lambda_j \geq 0$. Define
$$B = [B_j] = [A_1 + \lambda_1 A_{n+1}, \cdots, A_n + \lambda_n A_{n+1}]$$
and observe from the definition of the λ_j that $UB = 0$.

Since B has n columns it follows from the inductive hypothesis that there exist V and Y such that $VB \geq 0$, $Y \geq 0$, $BY = 0$, and $VB_1 + y_1 > 0$. With such V and Y define
$$\bar{Y} = \begin{bmatrix} Y \\ \sum_j \lambda_j y_j \end{bmatrix}, \qquad \mu = -\frac{VA_{n+1}}{UA_{n+1}}, \qquad \text{and} \qquad \bar{W} = V + \mu U.$$

The lemma will be established (with "U" $= \bar{W}$ and "X" $= \bar{Y}$) if we show that
$$\bar{W}A \geq 0, \qquad \bar{Y} \geq 0, \qquad \bar{A}\bar{Y} = 0, \qquad \text{and} \qquad \bar{W}A_1 + y_1 > 0.$$

Since $Y \geq 0$ and $\lambda_j \geq 0$ $(j = 1, \dots, n)$, we see that $\overline{Y} \geq 0$. Moreover,

$$\overline{AY} = \sum_{k=1}^{n} (B_k - \lambda_k A_{n+1})y_k + A_{n+1} \sum_{k=1}^{n} \lambda_k y_k = BY = 0.$$

To calculate $\overline{WA}$, we note first that, from the definition of μ, $\overline{WA}_{n+1} = 0$. Hence

$$\overline{WA} = [\overline{WA}, 0] = [\overline{WB}, 0].$$

From the definition of B, $UB = 0$. Since V was so chosen that $VB \geq 0$ we see that $\overline{WA} \geq 0$. Finally, again because $\overline{WA}_{n+1} = 0$ and $UB = 0$,

$$\overline{WA}_1 + y_1 = \overline{WB}_1 + y_1 = VB_1 + y_1,$$

and the last quantity is > 0 by the choice of V and Y. Lemma 1 is proved.

Lemma 2 ([12] p. 8). *For each* A *there exist* U *and* X *such that* $UA \geq 0$, $X \geq 0$, $AX = 0$, *and* $UA + X^t > 0$.

The last requirement is that $UA_j + x_j > 0$ $(j = 1, \dots, n)$. Lemma 1 refers to A_1 and x_1; denote the vectors of that lemma by U^1 and X^1. Repeat the application of Lemma 1 for $j = 2, \dots, n$, calling the respective vectors U^j and X^j. Define

$$U = \sum_{j=1}^{n} U^j$$

and

$$X = \sum_{j=1}^{n} X^j.$$

Since $U^j A \geq 0$, $X^j \geq 0$, and $AX^j = 0$ for $j = 1, \dots, n$, it is clear that $UA \geq 0$, $X \geq 0$, and $AX = 0$. Finally, for each j,

$$UA + X^t = \Sigma_k (U^k A + X^{kt}) \geq U^j A_j + x_j^j > 0;$$

here x_j^j is the jth component of X^j. Lemma 2 is proved.

Lemma 3 ([12] p. 11). *For each* A *there exist* U *and* X *such that* $U \geq 0$, $UA \geq 0$, $X \geq 0$, $-AX \geq 0$, $U^t - AX > 0$, *and* $UA + X^t > 0$.

Let I denote the $m \times m$ identity matrix and apply Lemma 2 to $\overline{A} = [I, A]$, obtaining U and $\overline{X}$ such that

$$U\overline{A} \geq 0, \qquad \overline{X} \geq 0, \qquad \overline{AX} = 0, \qquad \text{and} \qquad U\overline{A} + \overline{X}^t > 0;$$

define V and X by writing $\overline{X} - [V, X^t]^t$. Explicitly, in turn, these conditions yield first

$$U[I, A] = [U, UA] \geq 0,$$

whence $U \geq 0$ and $UA \geq 0$. Since $\overline{X} \geq 0$, both $X \geq 0$ and $V \geq 0$. Then the relation

$$\overline{AX} = [I, A] \begin{bmatrix} V^t \\ X \end{bmatrix} = [V^t + AX] = 0$$

implies that

$$-AX = V^t \geq 0.$$

Finally, the relation

$$U\bar{A} + \bar{X}^t = [U, UA] + [V, X^t] = [U + V, UA + X^t] > 0$$

implies that

$$UA + X^t > 0 \qquad \text{and} \qquad U^t + V^t = U^t - AX > 0,$$

completing the proof of Lemma 3.

Lemma 4 ([12] p. 13). *If* K *is a skew matrix (that is,* $K^t = -K$*), then there exists a column vector* W *such that* $W \geq 0$*,* $KW \geq 0$*, and* $KW + W > 0$*.*

Apply Lemma 3 to $A = -K$, obtaining vectors $U \geq 0$ and $X \geq 0$ such that

$$-UK \geq 0, \qquad KX \geq 0, \qquad U^t + KX > 0, \qquad \text{and} \qquad -UK + X^t > 0.$$

Define $W = U^t + X$; clearly $W \geq 0$, for that is true of both U and X. Next, from $KX \geq 0$ and $KU^t = -(UK)^t \geq 0$ it follows that $KW \geq 0$. Finally, $KX + U^t > 0$ and $KU^t + X > 0$ imply that $KW + W > 0$, completing the proof.

Following closely the discussion of [12] pp. 58ff., we use Lemma 4 to prove two further lemmas that lead at once to the basic theorems about the following dual pair of linear programming problems:

Primal	Dual
Maximize	Minimize
CX	UB
with	with
$X \geq 0$ and $AX \leq B$	$U \geq 0$ and $UA \geq C$

The first step is to use A, B, and C to construct a skew matrix of order $m + n + 1$:

$$K = \begin{bmatrix} 0 & -A & B \\ A^t & 0 & -C^t \\ -B^t & C & 0 \end{bmatrix} = -K^t.$$

By Lemma 4 there is a column vector $W = [V, Y^t, q]^t$, with q a scalar, such that

$$W \geq 0, \qquad KW \geq 0, \qquad \text{and} \qquad KW + W > 0.$$

On substituting the expressions for W and K in the last two relations we find six inequalities:

(a)	$AY \leq qB,$	(d)	$VB < CY + q,$
(b)	$qC \leq VA,$	(e)	$AY < qB + V^t,$
(c)	$VB \leq CY,$	(f)	$qC < VA + Y^t.$

The symbols W, V, Y, q, and (a) to (f) will have henceforth the meanings just designated.

Since they come directly from Lemma 4, the inequalities (a) to (f) do not depend on the constraints of the programming problem. At the same time, the condition $W \geq 0$ implies that $Y \geq 0$ and $V \geq 0$ (and $q \geq 0$). Thus Y and V will be feasible vectors for the respective problems if the further requirements $AY \leq B$ and $UA \geq C$ are met. Whether or not this is so depends in a striking way on whether $q > 0$ or $q = 0$.

Lemma 5. *If* $q > 0$ *then the programming problems have optimal vectors* X_M *and* U_m *such that* $U_m B = CX_M$, $AX_M < U_m^t + B$, *and* $C < U_m A + X_M^t$.

Divide inequalities (a) to (f) by q and define $X_M = Y/q$ and $U_m = V/q$. From (a) and (b) it now follows that X_M and U_m are feasible. But if X and U are any feasible vectors for the respective problems then it follows from the constraints that

$$CX \leq UAX \leq UB,$$

and we therefore see from (c) that

$$U_m B = CX_M.$$

The strict inequalities of the present lemma (which are not used later) follow respectively from (e) and (f).

Now suppose that $q = 0$. Then (a), (b), and (d) read $AY \leq 0$, $0 \leq VA$, and $VB < CY$. If X and U were feasible for the primal and dual problems respectively, a contradiction could be obtained. It would follow from (b), the primal constraints, the fact that $0 \leq V$, and (d) that

$$0 \leq VAX \leq VB < CY;$$

and from (a), the dual constraints, and the fact that $Y \geq 0$, that

$$0 \geq UAY \geq CY,$$

an apparent contradiction. We conclude that one problem or the other has inconsistent constraints.

If neither set of constraints is consistent then there is no feasible vector and a fortiori no optimal vector for either problem. We saw in the text (Sec. 3) that it is possible for one set of constraints to be consistent while the other is inconsistent. Can one problem have an optimal vector while the other has no feasible vectors? This cannot happen.

Suppose, for example, that X were feasible for the primal problem—that is, that $X \geq 0$ and $AX \leq B$. Let $z \geq 0$ be a scalar parameter and consider $Z = X + zY$; clearly $Z \geq 0$. Since $AY \leq 0$ by (a) and $z \geq 0$,

$$AZ = AX + zAY \leq AX \leq B.$$

Thus Z is feasible for each $z \geq 0$ and the set F of feasible points is unbounded. At the same time $CZ = CX + zCY$ and it follows, since $CY > 0$ (a conclusion that depended only on the feasibility of X), that CZ is not bounded above on F; an optimal vector cannot exist. We have proved the following statement.

Lemma 6. *If* $q = 0$ *then in the dual pair of programming problems either the primal or the dual constraints are inconsistent. If the primal constraints are consistent* (and hence the dual constraints inconsistent) *then the set* F *of feasible points is unbounded and the objective function is not bounded above on* F; *similarly if the dual constraints are consistent and the primal are inconsistent. Neither programming problem has an optimal vector.*

Lemmas 5 and 6 lead at once to the theorems that have been our main goal in this appendix.

Duality Theorem. *A feasible* X *for the primal programming problem* (or a feasible *U* for the dual problem) *is optimal if and only if there exists a feasible* U *for the dual problem* (or a feasible *X* for the primal problem) *such that* UB = CX; *such a feasible* U (or *X*) *is an optimal vector for the dual* (or primal) *problem.*

Suppose, in fact, that X is feasible for the primal problem. If X is optimal then by Lemma 6 $q > 0$ and the existence of the required feasible (indeed optimal) U such that $UB = CX$ follows from Lemma 5. That the stated condition is sufficient follows immediately, as was noted in the text (Sec. 3), from the inequality displayed above in the proof of Lemma 5.

Existence Theorem. *In order that one problem of a dual pair, and hence both, may have an optimal vector, it is necessary and sufficient that each problem have a feasible vector.*

The necessity of the stated condition is evident from the duality theorem. If each problem has a feasible vector then by Lemma 6 $q > 0$ and therefore Lemma 5 delivers optimal vectors X_M and U_m.

Resting as it does on Lemmas 1 to 4, the existence theorem is a constructive one. Let us start with an $m \times n$ matrix A, and vectors B and C, and suppose, as usual, that we wish to maximize CX subject to the constraints $X \geqq 0$ and $AX \leqq B$. A feasible vector X is determined by the values of n variables x_j ($j = 1, \cdots, n$), subject to the $m + n$ constraints $AX \leqq B$ and $X \geqq 0$. We shall follow the steps back through the lemmas, attempting as we go along to estimate very roughly the magnitude of the computational problem.

The first step is to construct the $(m + n + 1) \times (m + n + 1)$ skew matrix K. We then seek the vector W of Lemma 4, which has $m + n + 1$ components subject to $3(m + n + 1)$ linear conditions. The vector W is constructed from the vectors U and X of Lemma 3, and the matrix A there is now $- K$. Each of these two vectors has $m + n + 1$ components, and these $2(m + n + 1)$ variables are subject in Lemma 3 to a total of $6(m + n + 1)$ conditions. The vectors X and U are found by applying Lemma 2 to the $(m + n + 1) \times 2(m + n + 1)$ matrix $\overline{A} = [I, - K]$. In this application of Lemma 2, its vector U has $m + n + 1$ components and its vector X has $2(m + n + 1)$ components; these $3(m + n + 1)$ variables are subject to

$$(2 + 2 + 1 + 2)(m + n + 1) = 7(m + n + 1)$$

conditions. An examination of the proof of Lemma 2 reveals an even more threatening situation; each of the vectors U and X is the sum of $2(m + n + 1)$ vectors, each of which must be constructed individually by the recursive method used in the proof of Lemma 1. The recursive step in Lemma 1 from k to $k + 1$ is easy if the vector U available from step k and the column A_{k+1} have the property that $UA_{k+1} \geqq 0$; otherwise, we must calculate the λ's, form the matrix B, construct V and Y (in the proof) recursively, and so on.

The foregoing estimates neglect any computational advantage that may result from the facts that K is skew and that $\overline{A} = [I, -K]$. Nevertheless, they suggest a degree of complication that lends special appeal to a numerical method, such as the simplex method, that proceeds more directly to the desired result.